STRATA

How William Smith drew the First Map of the Earth in 1801 & Inspired the Science of Geology

To Jean

STRATA

How William Smith drew the First Map of the Earth in 1801 & Inspired the Science of Geology

John L. Morton

TEMPUS

First published 2001

PUBLISHED IN THE UNITED KINGDOM BY:

Tempus Publishing Ltd
The Mill, Brimscombe Port
Stroud, Gloucestershire GL5 2QG

PUBLISHED IN THE UNITED STATES OF AMERICA BY:

Tempus Publishing Inc.
2 Cumberland Street
Charleston, SC 29401
(Tel: 1-888-313-2665)

Tempus books are available in France, Germany and Belgium
from the following addresses:

Tempus Publishing Group
21 Avenue de la République
37300 Joué-lès-Tours
FRANCE

Tempus Publishing Group
Gustav-Adolf-Straße 3
99084 Erfurt
GERMANY

Tempus Publishing Group
Place de L'Alma 4/5
1200 Brussels
BELGIUM

British Library Cataloguing in Publication Data.
A catalogue record for this book is available from the British Library.

ISBN 0 7524 1992 7

Typesetting and origination by Tempus Publishing.
PRINTED AND BOUND IN GREAT BRITAIN.

Contents

Acknowledgements

I would like to express my gratitude to Dr. Ellis Owen, for many years a geologist and palaeontologist at the British Museum of Natural History, who first gave me the idea of writing this book; to my father, Leslie T. Morton, F.L.A., a former medical librarian, still actively involved in collating information and in authorship at the age of ninety-three, for his technical assistance; to David Goodger, who introduced me to a number of interesting relics of the Somersetshire Coal Canal; to my wife, Jean, for her unstinting support in all I try to do; and to the many others who have encouraged me in the production of this work. A very great deal has been written about Smith, but all of the material has been aimed at covering a particular aspect of his life and work. This is to date the only full biography of him. I have borrowed freely from *Memoirs of William Smith, LL.D.*, London, 1844, by his nephew, John Phillips, and from Thomas Sheppard's *William Smith: his Maps and Memoirs*, Hull, 1920. There are many other sources of information.

John Morton

Foreword

by Dr Ellis F. Owen

Professor Adam Sedgwick, the President of the Geological Society of London, dubbed William Smith 'the Father of English Geology' in 1831, and students of the subject and those interested in the science have for many years referred to him as such. Strictly speaking, this is not a correct epithet, since the science of geology in its broadest interpretation embodies the study of minerals, igneous rocks, sedimentary rocks and fossilised animals and plants. Nearly all of these subjects have, in one way or another, received the attention of scholars since ancient times. Thus the science of geology can be said to have had a very long history, long before the birth of Smith. It would have been more appropriate, therefore, to have given William Smith the credit for being the first man to have realised the true significance of fossils in the correlation of sedimentary strata over a great distance. The 'Father of Stratigraphy' is a more suitable title used nowadays to describe this remarkable pioneer, whose name, in my estimation, should stand in line with those of James Watt, Stephenson and Trevithick.

John Morton has given a detailed and very readable account of the life and times of this great man. He has probed even deeper into the private life and misfortunes of Smith than any biographer has so far, and has brought to light the strength of character, the determination and deep faith in his own ideas which William Smith appears to have hidden behind a somewhat shy exterior. This author is to be congratulated on a biography of classic proportions.

List of illustrations

All pictures are from the author's collection

Preface

It is really quite remarkable that the name of William Smith is not familiar to the British man-in-the-street. He was, after all, a great pioneer in a new science. He may not quite rank with Newton or Darwin, but his work was of great importance in the development of knowledge about the nature of rocks and strata, the fossils they contain and their significance to the country's economy. He is buried in an unmarked grave in Northampton, and seems to have been almost totally forgotten by all but those who have studied the history of geology. I sincerely hope that this book will help to rectify this great injustice to a man of vision, who had none of the financial advantages of the gentlemen collectors of curiosities and dilettanti of the eighteenth and nineteenth centuries. He was shunned by some of the privileged gentry because of his humble origin, although the more discerning contemporaries – the Duke of Bedford, Coke of Holkham and others - realised how important his knowledge and experience were and how useful he could be to them in improving their land and its productivity.

It is necessary to try to picture the times in which Smith lived – few roads, sailing ships, only the beginnings of railways in his last few years, the first stirrings of the Industrial Revolution but still much reliance on the horse, and a huge gap between the privileged rich and educated landowners and the ordinary people. The Napoleonic Wars were being waged, causing a drain on the country's economy. (Following a call to arms to 'crush the pride and insolence of France', Smith enlisted in the volunteers and attended three parades). The belief at that time was that rocks with marine fossils were sediments resulting from Noah's Flood, which the contemporary church taught took place in 3290BC. It was beginning to become clear that the time required for all the strata to be deposited one on top of the other had to be longer than the period during which the world was inundated, and infact longer than the 5,000 years that had elapsed since! The fossils were accepted as 'the antediluvian exuviae' of ancient creatures. They were, therefore, older than the strata in which they were found, which of course made no sense, yet this had to be accepted because of the conventional belief in the literal interpretation in the Book of Genesis.

The harnessing of mechanical power was changing the entire social structure of eighteenth-century Britain. Until now, wind, water and horses had had to do, but Matthew Boulton and James Watt had developed steam engines and these required energy of a different sort. Coal was the obvious candidate and there were numerous mines in Somerset, not far from where Smith had made his home whilst undertaking the survey of a local estate. While he was so employed, and later when he was called in to survey some of these mines, he lodged at Rugbourne Farm, near High Littleton, for some five years. He called it 'the birthplace of English geology', and he may well have had a presentiment of the significance of the discoveries he was later to make and of his developing ideas. Much later in life he was to earn from the President of the Geological Society of London the epithet 'the Father of English Geology'.

He was able to build on his knowledge of the geological structure of the area south-west of Bath, during his work in the coal-mines there. He created a nomenclature for several of the strata, much of which is still in use today – lias, forest marble, cornbrash and oolite all originate from him. By 1796, he was the first Briton to observe that rock strata could be traced for great distances and that the same succession of fossil groups from older to younger rocks could be found in many parts of England. He reasoned that, if the fossil content was the same, the rocks must be of similar age. He called this the principle of faunal succession, a tool that was later used to map out the geological history of the Earth and to identify such periods as the Cambrian and the Devonian. Smith also laid down one of the basic tenets of stratigraphical geology, the principle of superposition - if one series of rocks lies above another, then the upper was formed after the lower, unless it can be proved that the beds have been inverted by tectonic actions such as folding.

This book includes many quotations from Smith's published and unpublished works and other documents. These have been taken from the original and, understandably, contain many spelling, punctuation and capitalisation errors. These are reproduced in order to show Smith's usage of the language and some of his shortcomings. Some of them may, of course, be in the style of the time in which they were written.

This biography is not intended to be a scientific reference book down to the finest detail. It is, however, written as accurately as I have been able, and I hope it makes interesting reading and paints a comprehensive picture of the life and works of a great man of science. So that the text reads more comfortably, I have omitted dates of birth and death for the personalities of whom I have made mention. However, where I have been able to ascertain them, I have featured them in the index. I have also included an appendix listing the fossils which Smith first named. A second appendix lists Smith's principal publications and manuscripts. The titles of many of these are very long and unsuitable for the index, but appear generally in chronological order in the script, so should not be difficult to find. The third appendix has details of the whereabouts of any buildings or structures connected with Smith's life and work, for those who might like to follow the 'William Smith trail', and a fourth delineates the geological periods for easy reference.

John Morton
February 2001

1

The making of 'Strata Smith'

William Smith was born on 23 March 1769 in Churchill, a village twenty-five miles north-west of Oxford. John,William's father, was the village blacksmith and 'a very ingenious mechanic' who was the descendant of several generations of small land-owning farmers. His father had married Lucy Raleigh, a relation of the sixteenth-century adventurer, Sir Walter Raleigh. John's grandfather had settled on his daughter-in-law a parcel of land in Churchill amounting to nearly ten acres. William's mother, Anne, of Longcompton in Gloucestershire, was the daughter of another (unrelated) William Smith. William was the eldest of her five children, two girls and three boys. Their father died in 1777, when William was only seven, but his mother was a kind and able lady who brought up her family well, and William was devoted to her. She married again and lived until 1807.

William attended the village school, but could only benefit from a basic syllabus in reading, writing and simple arithmetic. He was blessed with remarkable memory and did well at school, although he was often given to quiet solitary rambles and, even at a young age, collecting fossils. He knew them by their local names – 'pundibs' (fossil mollusc shells) and 'poundstones' (petrified sea urchins), which dairymaids used to hold down the covers of earthen crocks of cheese. This obsession sometimes interfered with his work in the classroom; he left school at the age of eleven.

William had strong, clear memories of his early life lasting into his mature years. He recalled how, on his way to London at the age of twelve, he had seen the quarrying of chalk at Henley-on-Thames and noted how the full trucks on an inclined plane were used to bring the empty ones back up. He spent two years in London, returning to stay with his uncle William on his estate at Over Norton, a few miles to the north-east of Churchill. He begged him to buy him books on geometry and surveying, but the elder William, a practical farmer with few aspirations, could not see their value. Young William persisted, and his uncle reluctantly conceded. His nephew was later to show him that a good use of surveying techniques could help to plan drainage of waterlogged ground and

1. Manor House, Stow-On-The-Wold, where Smith lived with Edward Webb.

2. Signpost on the road from High Littleton to Timsbury.

3. Rugbourne Farm, High Littleton,Smith's lodgings from 1792–1795.

turn it into useful pasture. Although he was impressed, he still insisted on young William applying himself to productive farmwork. However, the lad continued his studies of geometry and practised drawing and colouring his work, in preparation for a career as an engineer and surveyor.

In 1787, Edward Webb, from Stow-on-the-Wold, a market town about six miles west of Churchill, was charged with making a detailed survey of the parish as part of the programmes of enclosures. He employed Smith, then eighteen, as his assistant and was so pleased with his work that he found him a permanent place in his business. This was a great turning point in William's life. He went to live with Webb in Manor House at the north end of Market Square in Stow.

There is no record of Smith having served as an apprentice to Edward Webb, a skilled mechanic and mathematician who invented and made several instruments of his trade. William worked for Webb for five years and clearly became well versed in the theory and practice of surveying. Webb was confident enough to entrust him with the management of much of his business. He gained a good knowledge of the soils and geological structure of Gloucestershire, Hampshire, Oxfordshire, Warwickshire, Worcestershire and Wiltshire. He was also able to see the workings of a new coal mine at Plaitford in the north of the New Forest. By the age of twenty-two he had recognised the

MEMORANDUMS, OBSERVATIONS, and Appointments, in SEPTEMBER, 1789.

7 Monday	at Stow) Mr Webb and I making a Key of the Numbers of the Qualitys at each price in each sort of Land in L. Swell Field to prepare it for the collecting Sheets
8 Tuesday	Writing in the sheets the Numbers of the Qualitys from the said Key and ruling some more sheets and [illegible] them the same
9 Wednesday	Mr Webb & I began to
10 Thursday	collect the Particulars of each Persons Property
11 Friday	and Roads &c at each price in each sort of Land in
12 Saturday	Lower Swell Fields
13 Sunday	Went to Churchill [illegible] ~~Came back to Stow~~

4. A page from Smith's diary, 1789.

Lias, the Trias and the Carboniferous rocks of mid-Somerset. In 1791, Webb sent William to survey and value an estate at Stowey, south-west of Bath. He walked - noting the geology on the way - the sixty miles from Stow to High Littleton, where he lodged at Rugbourne (formerly Rugborne) Farm until 1795. His rent was 'half-a-guinea a week, plus half-a-crown for his horse'. The house, a listed building of three storeys with the top floor windows filled in, remains almost unchanged since he lived there. Smith's association with it is recalled on a signpost to it on the road from High Littleton to Timsbury.

Smith took a particular interest in the geology of the countryside around his new home. Over the next two years, he was involved in inspecting and drawing up detailed plans of some of the many coal-mines in the area. Among the papers marshalled after his death by his nephew, John Phillips, was an *Original Sketch and Observations of my first Subterranean Survey of Mearns Colliery in the parish of High Littleton*. There was also a proposal to

> make a model of the strata of earth and coal at High Littleton, of the same materials of which they are composed, reduced to scale and planed in the same order in which they are found in sinking of pits

and to 'make a section of it' so that it could be taken apart to explain how the coal should be mined.

He made sure he understood well the methods applied to the construction of new canals, such as the use of locks and caissons (large watertight cases used in laying foundations under water, not to be confused with the 'caisson' locks we shall shortly encounter). He also drew a map of High Littleton, which is extant.

The Somersetshire Coal Canal

John Rennie, a Scottish civil engineer, had become famous as a bridge-builder. He had drained fens, designed the docks in London, improved harbours and dockyards at Portsmouth, Chatham and Plymouth, and planned and saw constructed many important canals - including the Kennet and Avon, opened in 1810, which linked Bristol with London, via the Thames. He was to plan the construction of a new canal to carry coal from the collieries south-west of Bath to join up with the Kennet and Avon near Limpley Stoke. In 1793, he gave William Smith, at the age of twenty-four, the responsibility of the necessary surveys for the levelling work. In undertaking this, Smith was able to verify that the strata above the coal were not horizontal, but dipped towards the east, giving the appearance of 'superimposed slices of bread and butter'. Smith knew, and was able to confirm by an inspection of the mine at Pucklechurch in Gloucestershire, that the coal strata did not conform to those above them, and that faults in the coal seams did not extend to the later rocks. He was at first puzzled by this, but not for long. He realised that there had been a considerable lapse of time between the formation of the peat, later to become coal, and the next stratum of rock being laid down over it. In the interim, the peat layer had been partially eroded.

In March 1794, Smith travelled to London to give evidence to Parliament to ease the passing of the Act authorising the construction of the canal. There were to be two branches about six miles long, running roughly parallel to each other along the valleys of the Cam and Wellow Brooks, linking up at Midford and

5. One of the 22 derelict locks on the Somersetshire Coal Canal, Combe Hay.

continuing to Limpley Stoke. Later that year, Smith and two Members of the Board of the canal company, Dr. Richard Perkins and Sambourne Palmer, went on a tour taking between one and two months to cover some 900 miles by carriage, as far north as Newcastle upon Tyne, to see other canals and collieries. Smith was delighted to have the opportunity to extend his knowledge of the geology of England and to confirm his ideas about the succession of strata, which interested him a great deal. He found that, in general, strata dipped to the east right across the country, and the succession in the north of England was similar to that in the area around Bath and Bristol. Where he was unable to inspect the rocks at close quarters, he felt confident he could identify them by the lie of the land and the nature of the flora. The trio also viewed the Sapperton Tunnel, four miles west of Cirencester on the Thames and Severn

6. Dunkerton Aqueduct on the Somersetshire Coal Canal.

Canal. This was just over two miles long and 280 feet below the surface, through the Oolitic Limestone (then called 'Stonebrash') of the Cotswold Hills. It was the longest canal transport tunnel in the country (and remains the third longest), an astounding achievement.

They also inspected a canal tunnel in King's Norton (then Kingsnorth), a suburb of Birmingham. It was to burrow 1.5 miles through Red Marl and New Red Sandstone, rocks familiar to them at High Littleton. Further north, they saw variegated columns of Millstone Grit at Chatsworth, the Limestone and Tufa at Matlock in Derbyshire and the Magnesian Limestone (previously unknown to them) on Tadcaster Moor, near York. They found small steam engines used for raising coal better applied in Yorkshire than in Somerset, and they had a practical demonstration of a cleverly-designed mechanism for carrying the miners down into the pit and back up again. They continued their journey to Newcastle, noting the geology on the way. At Heaton Colliery, just north of the River Tyne, they were shown how water was pumped up from the pit by steam engine into a pool on the surface. It was carried up from there by much larger pumps to a flume feeding two high water-wheels which were used to raise the coal. They noted the devices needed to ventilate the pit, something not necessary in Somerset due to a good circulation of air.

Work on the Somersetshire Coal Canal began in July 1795, and Smith remained in the employ of the company until 1799, at a salary of one guinea (£1.05) a day, with an allowance for extraordinary expenses. He became familiar with the strata through

7. Track of the Somersetshire Coal Canal, near Midford, and the aqueduct from the Northern Arm to the Tramway Transhipment Basin.

which the canal passed, from Triassic Marls (Calcareous Clay 213 to 248 million years old) to the Lias (blue-grey Shales and muddy Limestones of the early Jurassic epochs, 188 to 213 million years of age), and the Oolites of the same period. Smith himself named these particular forms of limestone which consist of sub-spherical, sand-sized particles with concentric rings of calcium carbonate surrounding a nucleus of another particle, and may be seen in many fine buildings in Bath and elsewhere. Smith realised that all these strata had been formed at the bottom of the sea. He noticed how undamaged the fossils in most deposits were, but how those that lay in gravel had been rounded and worn down, having been disturbed by the movement of water and the stones around them. He could see that these effects did not reach to any great depth and understood that they were the result of some sort of deluge, which might have been Noah's Flood. We know now, of course, that the damage resulted from their being carried along in the outflow of melting glaciers at the end of the geologically-recent Ice Age. Smith advised the contractors of the nature of the strata to be cut through and which parts of the canal would need extra care to ensure they remained leak-proof. He determined where materials for adequate foundations would be found to support bridges, where to discover suitable building stone, and how to intercept springs which might compromise the soundness of the structures.

To avoid the necessity of a three-quarters of a mile tunnel at Combe Hay, the Canal Company decided to build their cut on two levels, the western part near the coalfields being some 145 feet above the eastern section, the height of which was dictated by the

8. The lock at the junction of the Somersetshire Coal Canal, and the Kennet and Avon (which has fall of just seven inches).

requirement to join what was to become the Kennet and Avon Canal at the Dundas Aqueduct at Limpley Stoke (known to the locals as the 'huckyduck'). There was a lock here with a fall of only seven inches, solely to prevent water from the larger canal flowing into the new one.

This was an age of new technology, and Robert Weldon had recently patented a 'caisson lock'. This was at the time thought to be one of the 'wonders of the waterway world'. The original plan to join the two levels incorporated three of these new devices in series. They were large boxes, into which a boat would be floated. With its doors closed, the box would rise or descend in a lined chamber. The *Bath Herald* for 27 June 1795, described the caisson lock as follows;

> This ingenious contrivance consists of a wood cistern, having two square apertures with a slide door to each, at the respective levels of the upper and lower Canals; In this reservoir (being always full of water) is immersed a Caisson, or hollow vessel; having a door water-tight at each end, for the purpose of receiving and enclosing a boat; this Caisson is ballasted, to be specifically of the same gravity of water, consequently will descend or ascend in its surrounding medium (with or without a load) with the greatest facility. Each end of the Caisson, when brought in contact with the square apertures of the reservoir, is also water-tight; this is accomplished by an inverted valve, discharging the water from the

> space between the slide door of the reservoir and the door of the Caisson, the pressure instantly then fixes the Caisson to the apertures, therefore the slide-door may be opened with much ease, and of course that of the Caisson. The boat may then be received for ascension, the doors re-shut, and the great difficulty of releasing the Caisson from the aperture (against which it was so power-fully pressed) obviated, by opening another valve to refill the space just mentioned; it consequently follows, the pressure on the Caisson will be as before, equal on all its sides – by discharging a small quantity of water from the Caisson by means of a cock into the lower Canal, it becomes lighter and instantly ascends to the upper aperture; the same process with the valves completes the design which is truly philosophical.

In January 1796, advertisements appeared in the Bath press for masons to build a caisson lock at Combe Hay. William Smith visited the site in 1798 and 1799. Although the design was at first successful (it took only seven minutes to complete the passage of a boat), it was found to be very difficult to keep such a large container watertight because the boats were up to 72 ft long and over 7ft wide. The walls of the shaft were unstable, probably because they were cut through a stratum of Fuller's Earth, which became swollen when wet and caused them to bulge, trapping the caisson. They may also have collapsed entirely. One caisson lock had been completed and another started, at a cost of £4,582, when the Company was obliged to turn to the use of an inclined plane, in which empty containers were hauled uphill by the descent of full ones. This required the inefficient trans-shipment of goods, but was the only scheme available for the time being. The northern branch of the canal from High Littleton to Dundas Aqueduct, (the two levels being connected by the inclined plane), opened for traffic in 1801. In 1805, a flight of nineteen locks was added to an existing trio, built in the lead-up to the proposed 'caisson' locks, to replace the inclined plane. They were set close together in a loop up a short lateral valley at Combe Hay. This involved a 160° turn at what was called the Bull's Nose. Seven of these derelict locks are accessible to the public today but are generally in a poor state. The Somersetshire Coal Canal Society, founded in 1992, aims to protect these and other remaining structures, though they have no present ambition to restore the canal.

Work started at the collieries end on both arms, but only the first 5½ miles of the southern one, from Radstock to Twinhoe, were completed (in 1805). Because the Company would have had to build another extensive flight of locks and they had run out of money, they laid down a tramway to carry the goods from Twinhoe to a trans-shipment basin, fed by a short branch from the northern arm over an aqueduct near Midford, which today stands high and dry in the middle of a field. Eventually the tramway was extended back to Radstock, to replace this arm of the canal altogether, running along its towpath. The canal was one of the most successful in the country – by the 1820s it was carrying over 100,000 tons of coal a year, but the railways soon took a large part of its trade away, and it finally closed in 1898. Following a dispute with the

Company, William Smith was dismissed as Resident Engineer with them on 5 June, 1799, so he did not see the completion of his work. His dismissal may have been because it was considered that he should have known about the fuller's earth problem and spoken up sooner, especially as he had sided with the anti-caisson lobby. Or it may have been that he was mixing private interests and those of the Company in the purchase of a property at Tucking Mill, half a mile north-east of Midford. The canal was to run right in front of this, so he probably gained some satisfaction later from watching it in operation.

Smith was presumably a God-fearing man, for he often referred to the work of the Almighty and had several members of the clergy as close friends. The Church was, at that time,teaching that the Earth was created in 4004BC. This was based on a literal interpretation of the Book of Genesis made in the previous century by a Protestant Irish prelate working in London, James Ussher. The Church also taught that sedimentary rocks derived from silt laid down by Noah's Flood, and that 'fossils were the work of the Devil, put there to deceive, mislead or perplex mankind.' Several years after Ussher, John Lightfoot, a Hebrew scholar, confirmed the calculation and refined it to 9am on Sunday, 23 October, 4004BC! Smith understood that the fossils he was finding were the remains of antediluvial creatures, but had no inkling of just how old they were. He was unknowingly moving into a conflict with the Church's teaching, which would not manifest itself until Darwin's bombshell in 1859 in *The Origin of Species by Means of Natural Selection*. It is almost certain that Darwin was influenced by Smith's work.

While Smith had been in London to appear before Parliament, he had attempted to find books on geology, but come across very few. He may not therefore have been aware of James Hutton's geological work in Norfolk and Scotland. Hutton put forward his theory of uniformitarianism (paraphrased as 'the present is the key to the past', or that evidence in the rocks shows us that geological processes we see today have happened throughout the history of Earth), in his sketch of *a Theory of the Earth*, or *an Investigation of the Laws observable in the Composition, Dissolution and Restoration of Land upon the Globe*, presented to the Royal Society of Edinburgh in 1785. He used this as the basis for his famous work *The Theory of the Earth, with Proofs and Illustrations*, published in Edinburgh in two volumes later that year. He, too, was looking at fossils and their relationship to strata. Hutton introduced for the first time the idea of igneous rocks and their erosion over a vast period to form sedimentary deposits, which became consolidated and then in turn were uplifted again by volcanism. He realised that this would take a great deal longer than the 5,800 years since the Earth was supposed to have been formed and suggested that its history had developed across almost limitless time.

In 1795, Smith moved from High Littleton into the southern part of the city of Bath, where he lived in the central house of a short range of buildings called Cottage Crescent (now Bloomfield Crescent). This put him rather nearer to the eastern end of the canal, the operations in the construction of which he supervised so conscientiously that he could only find time to write down the briefest of notes on his discoveries in

9. Smith's house at Cottage Crescent, Bath.

geology. He spoke enthusiastically about them to anyone who would listen, and convinced the intelligent land-steward of the Marquis of Bath, Thomas Davis, that with regard to agriculture, 'that is the only way to know the true value of land.'

In 1796, Smith spent some time at the Swan Inn, Dunkerton in the Cam Brook valley. After a long day's work superintending the construction of the canal, he sat down on the evening of 5 January and wrote a note:

> Fossils have long been studdied as great curiossities [*sic*] collected with great pains treasured up with great care and at great Expence and shown and admired with as much pleasure as a Child's rattle or his Hobbyhorse is shown and admired by himself and his playfellows – because it is pretty. And this has been done by Thousands who have never paid the least regard to that wonderful order & regularity with which Nature has disposed of these singular productions and assigned to each Class its peculiar stratum.

Smith had come to realise that, unless disturbed by tectonic forces, strata occur in regular order, the lower ones being the older, and that the fossils they contain also manifest themselves in a similar régime, many being unique to each stratum (index fossils). This allowed correlation between layers of rock great distances apart and at different depths from the surface, whether in hillsides, quarries or canal cuts. Although this would seem to be obvious, nobody had expressed the idea before this twenty-six-year old 'plain and moderately-lettered man' did so. As much of what falls into the Cretaceous period belies its name and is not chalk but sandstone, its age might not readily be recognised but for Smith's index fossils. Smith had found a way of determining relative time; it was well into the twentieth century before what we now think of as accurate absolute dating became possible through the use of radioactive isotopes. Our subject soon became known as 'Strata Smith'. From Dunkerton, he published a list of twenty-three English strata from the Chalk to the Coal Measures and the Carboniferous Limestone beneath them, an age range as we now know of some 300 million years, together with details of the fossils they contained, including replacement fossils in the Oolite. (Replacement fossils are formed when an original shell is dissolved and simultaneously another mineral material is deposited – this may occur molecule by molecule, when the microstructure is preserved, or *en masse*, when it is not).

An extract from another of his papers, dated August 1797 and entitled *Locality of Plants, Insects, Birds, &c., arises from the nature of the strata* reads as follows:

> Where art has not diverted the order of things, and nature is left to herself, a considerable locality may be observed in many animals and vegetables, as well as mineral productions, by which they are evidently attached on particular soils to such a degree that, if this subject were studied with attention, it would form one of the principal external characteristics of the strata underneath. Though it may seem mysterious to some that birds, beasts, insects, &c., which have the liberty of roving at pleasure, should feel any particular attachment for this or that soil, yet the wonder ceases when we consider how the chain of natural things is linked together and how these creatures are taught to cull their food from insects that are lodged in, or seeds that are produced from, particular plants that grow upon particular soils.

On 3 November he recorded some of his fossils and the location where they were found (snakestones are what we now call ammonites):

> 1. Snakestone, 11 inches diameter. Found near the bottom of a rough bed of bastard freestone (Inferior Oolite), which lies upon a thick bed of sand and sand burs. Remarks.- The surface of this stone is covered with marks which have some resemblance to the leaves of plants [edges of the septa], but on breaking any stone of this sort these marks are found to represent natural divisions of the fossil, which are so linked or dovetailed one into another in this curious manner as not to be separated without violence after the joints are considerably loosened.
> 2. Part of a snakestone, about 4½inches diameter. Found in the same bed

> about two miles distant from the place where No.1 was found. Remarks.- The loose joint at the end of this stone will fully explain what I have said about the leaves and joints of No.1.
> 3. Snakestone, about 3 inches diameter, of a bluish cast. Found in the Blue Lias limestone.
> [The names he employed were those in use in the locality at the time. The ideas expressed were all his own].

In another manuscript written at the Swan Inn, Dunkerton, on 2 December, 1796, entitled *Strata in general and their position,* obviously meant for publication, he says:

> The strata being found as regular on one side of a rivulet, river, deep valley or channel as on the other, over an extent of many miles, when proper allowance is made for the inclination and for the variation of the surface, is it not reasonable to suppose that the same strata may be found as regular on one side of a sea or ocean as on opposite sides of a deep valley upon land, and if so, and the continuation of the strata is general, what is their general direction or drift? Is it in straight lines from pole to pole, or in curved lines surrounding the globe regularly inclined to the east?
>
> But all theories are best built on practical rules, which will enable anyone to make such observations for himself as must carry conviction along with them, for a work so novel as this must expect to find some who will hardly believe what is plain to be seen; for all men do not see alike, nor can patiently trudge through the dirt to search for truth among the stubborn rocks, where nature has best displayed her...Shall, therefore, describe a number of quarries, cliffs, &c., at a great distance, &c., See Book --.
>
> If the strata lay horizontal, every part of the sea-shores would present the same beds at the water edge instead of that wonderful variety which is found on the coast and banks of every river and rivulet in the kingdom, especially those that run in an east and west direction or nearly so. In such situations the young mineralogist may soon be convinced of that wonderful regularity which nature has adopted, especially if the shores are rocky; he will there find that, independent of partial and local dips which appear in different quarries of the same stone, the outlines or top and bottom layers of each complete stratum or class of stones or earth, considered as a mass, have a general tendency toward the eastern horizon.

In late 1796, Smith was admitted as a member of the Bath and West of England Society. This was an exclusive club of men of standing and intellectual achievement. Other new members that year were the Duke of Bedford, the Earl of Egremont and

10. Tucking Mill Cottage, near Midford, where Smith did not live, despite the plaque on its front wall.

11. Plaque on the front wall of Tucking Mill Cottage. Smith, in fact, lived at Tucking Mill House, 100 yards to the east.

12. Tucking Mill House, where Smith lived from 1798 to 1818.

the Earl of Peterborough. Considering his humble background and his young age, this must have been a great honour. He was able to meet and discuss with significant people his progress in geological research. It stood him in good stead when he was seeking employment as a land drainer after his agreement with the Coal Canal ended. He was later offered contracts by Coke of Holkham, the Dukes of Bedford and Manchester, the Earls of Thanet and of Talbot, and by Lord Somerville.

In 1888, a memorial tablet was put on the west wall of Tucking Mill (near Smith) by the Bath Natural History and Antiquarian Field Club, but the building was pulled down in 1927 and the tablet mislaid. After it was rediscovered, it was re-erected on the south-east wall of a dwelling house in South Stoke parish in 1932 by the Geological Society of London and the Bath Royal Literary and Scientific Institution. In her comprehensively-researched article *William Smith's home near Bath: the real Tucking Mill,* Joan M. Eyles (1974) shows conclusively that it was placed on the wrong building and should have been on a nearby property. As long ago as 1974, Joan Eyles urged that the tablet be moved from its position on Tucking Mill Cottage (scheduled as a building of historical interest) to the correct house about a hundred yards to the east and in the next parish (Monkton Combe), though nothing has been done. The right building is

13. Smith's geological mao of the district near Bath, 1799.

14. 29 Great Pulteney Street, Bath, where Smith dictated his Table of Strata in 1799.

now called Tucking Mill House. The ownership of this house by Smith from 1798 to 1818 is shown in the land tax returns for Monkton Combe. A slight increase in his land tax in 1806 indicates that Smith bought a small plot of land from his neighbour to the west, Stephen Slade of Trowbridge, probably for the construction in part of a mill pond, because letters written between 1808 and 1810 show that Smith had a tenant, James Sutton, who was constructing a mill. Tucking Mill House was built in two phases. Smith owned what is now the westerly half, the other part being added later. It is thought that William Smith's brother, John, lived in Tucking Mill Cottage from 1811, when he was put in charge of the operation of the freestone quarry they set up in Kingham Field on Summer Lane, behind Tucking Mill House.

During his first few years of ownership of Tucking Mill House, Smith spent about twelve months living a mile or so away at Midford (then Mitford), carrying out his duties as resident engineer on the Coal Canal. In later years he was absent from his home for a considerable time, working in various parts of the country, but having felled trees, cleared the ground, planted the garden and constructed the pond, he held the property in great affection. In 1825, when he was living in Yorkshire, he recalled it in verse:

Tucking Mill

I made the woodman's axe resound
The oaks were levelled to the ground
The thorn & briar crack'd on the fire
The goodly ground was cleared
And fruits and garden shrubs appeared.
Great Plans were laid, a fish pond made
Combining taste with trade
That wandering path which leads to Bath
Contrived to ease the hill
And Freestone Blocks torn from the rocks
Run down to yonder mill.
0 Tucking Mill I love thee still
And oft afar in fancy trace
My musings there beneath thy bower
'Tis contemplation's place.
The mazy round of varied ground

The coolness of thy caves
In hollow rocks & fossil blocks...

The name of the mill comes from its activity – the cleaning and thickening (or fulling) of freshly-woven woollen fabric. There was, until well into this century, a fuller's earth works behind Tucking Mill Cottage.

2

The First Map of the Earth

Smith started to make coloured maps of the regional geology, showing how the various strata outcropped. He began with one of the area around Bath in 1799 which he presented to the Geological Society in 1831. The basic map which he used appeared in *The Historic and Local New Bath Guide* and he almost certainly obtained it from this source, adding the colours. It was circular, covering a radius of five miles (eight km) around Bath on a scale of 1½ inches to one mile. Professor J.W. Judd wrote in the *Geological Magazine* in 1897:

> Though no lines are drawn, Smith's well-known method of covering the base of a formation with a deep tint, and shading this upwards towards the outcrop of the next overlying stratum, enables us to see how carefully he had mapped all the geological lines around Bath. There are only three colours employed on the map and no index; but it is evident that the yellow tint represents the Bath Oolite, the base of the freestones being very accurately mapped so that even the smallest outlines can be made out agreeing most closely with the map of the Geological Survey; a blue tint is drawn at the base of the Lias, and a red one at the base of the Trias, the inliers of the Carboniferous being left blank.

The map is said to be the oldest geological map in existence. It is hung in the library of the Geological Society in Burlington House in Piccadilly, London. Two others, clearly of similar date, were found amongst Smith's papers at Oxford University Museum in 1938. At about the same time, he had coloured in the geology of Somerset on a map published by Day and Masters on a scale of one inch to one mile. Unfortunately this has not survived. The Ordnance Survey did not begin publication until 1801, starting with Kent and taking seventy years to cover the entire country, so nothing was available from that source for some time, but for many of his later maps Smith was able to use those of the London publisher, John Cary. The details shown helped him to mark in geological boundaries accurately.

Soon after his engagement with the Canal Company was terminated in 1799, Smith struck up a close friendship with the Rev. Benjamin Richardson, Rector of Farleigh Hungerford, an avid fossil collector who lived in Bath, and whom he had met at the annual meeting of the Bath Agricultural Society. It was a fortuitous partnership, because Richardson was extremely knowledgeable in natural history but had little understanding of the laws of stratification and the connection between the forms of organic life and the order of superposition, while Smith's observations completed the picture. Between them they were able to marshall Richardson's fine collection of fossils into the correct order of the strata in which they were found. Smith was able to convince him that everywhere throughout the district, and for considerable distances around, it was a general law that the 'same strata were found always in the same order of superposition and contained the same peculiar fossils.' Richardson was, in return, able to help Smith with the names of fossils in his collection.

Richardson introduced Smith to a widely-travelled friend, the Rev. Joseph Townsend of Pewsey, also a keen fossil collector, and the three of them went out on field trips to verify what Smith was claiming. To this end, on 11 December 1799, they visited the hill at Dundry (south-west of Bristol), which is capped by the Inferior Oolite, intending to confirm that the rock contained the same fossils as it did near Bath. Needless to say, this was so. This naturally convinced Smith's two new friends that here was something new and important. After dining together at Townsend's home in Bath, they determined that an ordered list of strata identified by Smith should be drawn up in writing. Richardson wrote down to Smith's dictation his *Table of Strata near Bath*, from the chalk down to the coal measures, below which little was known about at the time. Smith gave names not only to the Oolites but also to several other strata, and these are still in use today. To this list were added the most remarkable fossils found in each layer. The names of these were supplied by Richardson. Copies were made and widely distributed to interested parties, including Baron Rosencrantz, and Dr. Muller of Christiania (now Oslo). Sir John Flett remarks in his *Pioneers of British Geology*:

> Nothing so complete and convincing had been seen before. It marks the beginning of scientific stratigraphical geology and entitles Smith to the title of Father of British Stratigraphy. That a man who possessed only an elementary education, had of his own initiative, and entirely unassisted, accomplished an achievement so difficult, so original, and so important, is one of the wonders of the history of science.

This famous list and a geologically-coloured map by Smith are held by the Geological Society of London, to which he presented them in 1831.

Richardson also introduced Smith to Dr. James Anderson, who was about to publish his *Recreations in Agriculture*. The doctor tried to persuade Smith to publish his findings, offering him inclusion in his book, but the latter did not feel confident enough of his literary skill, rather hoping for some assistance in this area from the author himself, but he received none.

Around the middle of the twentieth century, an unrecorded manuscript in Smith's handwriting was discovered at Oxford. It was a list of strata compiled by him at least two years before the one he dictated to Rev. Benjamin Richardson, and was clearly a preliminary outline of the second part of Smith's proposed treatise on the stratified rocks of England. J.A. Douglas and L.R. Cox published it in the *Geology Magazine*, **86**, 1949. There are a number of omissions where later corrections have obliterated the original script, and annotations by the authors have been included in brackets where they apply, rather than at the end. Spellings, capitalisations and punctuation are as they appear in the script, which begins with four different potential titles:

> *Natural order of the Strata or Structure of the Earth deduced from practical Observations from which are also drawn some Remarks on the Deluge part 2nd.*
>
> Or
>
> *Strata of the Earth delineated in its Natural Order by Wm. Smith Landsurveyor*
>
> *Strata of the Earth delineated from Observations Of Nature by Wm. Smith Landsurveyor*
>
> *An accurate delineation of Terraqueous Strata from observations on Nature by W. S. - Landsurveyor.*
>
> Aug. 15th 1797
>
> No 1 *Chalk Strata*. As the immense Quantity of Chalk which composes that range of high Hills that stretch from the low Grounds inshire thro' Bedfordshire Buckinghamshire Berkshire Wiltshire and Dorsetshire to the Sea forms one of the leading features of this kingdom - I intend to make those Hills the leading feature of this work and by making It the first Number in my list of the Strata this being a bed whose colour nor quality cannot be mistaken making it much fitter for that purpose than any Stratum I am yet acquainted with more especially as my observations have hitherto been confined chiefly to the Western side of these hills.
>
> No 2 *1st Bed of Sand & Sandstone, from the Chalk* [the Upper Greensand]. This Stratum of Sand found near the foot of the

No. I.—Order of the STRATA and their imbedded ORGANIC REMAINS, in the vicinity of BATH; examined and proved prior to 1799.

Strata.	Thickness.	Springs.	Fossils, Petrifactions, &c. &c.	Descriptive Characters and Situations.
1. Chalk	300	Intermitting on the Downs	Echinites, pyrites, mytilites, dentalia, funnel-shaped corals and madrepores, nautilites, strombites, cochliæ, ostreæ, serpulæ	Strata of Silex, imbedded.
2. Sand	70			The fertile vales intersecting Salisbury Plain and the Downs.
3. Clay	30	Between the Black Dog and Berkeley.		
4. Sand and Stone	30			Imbedded is a thin stratum of calcareous grit. The stones flat, smooth, and rounded at the edges.
5. Clay	15	Hinton, Norton, Woolverton, Bradford Leigh.		
6. Forest Marble	10		A mass of anomiæ and high-waved cockles, with calcareous cement	The cover of the upper bed of freestone, or oolite.
7. Freestone	60		Scarcely any fossils besides the coral	Oolite, resting on a thin bed of coral.—Prior Park, Southstoke, Twinny, Winsley, Farley Castle, Westwood, Berfield, Conkwell, Monkton Farley, Coldhorn, Marshfield, Coldashton.
8. Blue Clay	6	Above Bath.		
9. Yellow Clay	8			
10. Fuller's Earth	6			Visible at a distance, by the slips on the declivities of the hills round Bath.
11. Bastard ditto, and Sundries	80		Striated cardia, mytilites, anomiæ, pundibs and duck-muscles.	
12. Freestone	30		Top-covering anomiæ with calcareous cement, strombites, ammonites, nautilites, cochliæ hippocephaloides, fibrous shell resembling amianth, cardia, prickly cockle, mytilites, lower stratum of coral, large scollop, nidus of the muscle with its cables	Lincombe, Devonshire Buildings, Englishcombe, Englishbatch, Wilmerton, Dunkerton, Coomhay, Monkton Coombe, Wellow, Mitford, Stoke, Freshford, Claverton, Bathford, Batheaston and Hampton, Charlcombe, Swanswick, Tadwick, Langridge.
13. Sand	30		Ammonites, belemnites	Sand burs.
14. Marl Blue	40	Round Bath.	Pectenites, belemnites, gryphites, high-waved cockles	Ochre balls.—Mineral springs of Lincombe, Middle Hall, Cheltenham.
15. Lias Blue	25		Same as the marl with nautilites, ammonites, dentalia, and fragments of the enchrini	The fertile marl lands of Somersetshire. Twerton, Newton, Preston, Clutton, Stanton Prior, Timsbury, Paulton, Marksbury, Farmborough, Corston, Hunstreet, Burnet, Keynsham, Whitchurch, Salford, Kelston, Weston, Pucklechurch, Queencharlton, Norton-malreward, Knowle, Charlton, Kilmersdon, Babington.
16. Ditto White	15			
17. Marl Stone, Indigo and Black Marl	15		Pyrites and ochre	A rich manure.
18. Red-ground	180		No fossil known	Pits of riddle. Beneath this bed no fossil, shells, or animal remains are found: above it no vegetable impressions. The waters of this stratum petrify in the trunks which convey it, so as to fill them, in about fifteen years, with red watricle, which takes a fine polish.—Highlittleton.
19. Millstone.				
20. Pennant Street			Impressions of unknown plants resembling equisetum.	
21. Grays				Fragments of coal and iron nodules.—Hanham, Brislington, Mangotsfield, Downend, Winterbourn, Forest of Dean, Pensford, Publow, Chelwood, Cumptondando, Hallatrow near Stratford-on-Avon, Stonebench on the Severn, four miles from Gloucester.
22. Cliff			Impressions of ferns, olive, stellate plants, threnax-parviflora, or dwarf fan-palm of Jamaica	Stourbridge, or fire-clay.
23. Coal				

15. Smith's Order of the Strata, 1799, as printed in Phillips's Memoirs.

Chalk hills is well known as the basis or under Stratum to the Fertile Sandy Land described in Mr. Davis's [Thomas Davis of Longleat, Land Steward to the Marquess of Bath and author of the Board of Agriculture Report *General View of the Agriculture of Wiltshire*] very sensible report on the state of agriculture in Wiltshire.

No.3 *Clay* [probably the Gault. At this period Smith had met with this formation in a brickyard at Crockerton, south-west of Warminster, and in an exposure near the Black Dog Inn, south of Standerwlck, on the Warminster-Bath road. He may also have seen exposures of the Oxford or Kellaways [sic] Clay [named after Kelloways Bridge in Wiltshire] and confused them with the Gault. This Stratum of Clay or perhaps [sentence uncompleted].

No.4 *Stratum of fine Sand* [No doubt No.4 referred to some exposure of beds of the Forest Marble series. The brief description given does not quite tally with the typical Hinton Sand of the Hinton Charterhouse district, which constituted Stratum 4 of Smith's 1799 list of a lightish yellow colour with thin Beds of Stone (used for paving and slate) imbeded [sic].

No.5 *Thin Beds of shelly Wall Stone* [the Forest Marble. It may be noted that this name is not used in the present list, although introduced in the 1799 list] imbed in Clay or clayey sand.

No.6 *Upper Bed of Bastard Freestone* [the Bath Stone. When this MS. was written Smith was living at Cottage Crescent, on the northern flank of Odd Down, Bath, and there were several Bath Stone quarries in the immediate neighbourhood. He goes, however, astray in correlating this formation with the freestone (Chipping Norton Limestone) quarried near his native village of Churchill, in North Oxfordshire. In a note added in 1799 to the present MS. he goes still further astray in correlating the Bath Stone with the freestone (Inferior Oolite) of Frocester and Birdlip Hills, in the Cotswolds]. I think the Rubbishey Stone-brash Beds nr. Churchill &c which lie immediately upon a Strong Blue Clay must be the same as the bottom Beds of the Rocks near Cottage Crescent &c in Somersetshire.

No.7 *Blue Clay with Talk imbeded.* [Formations 7 and 8 are now grouped together as Upper Fuller's Earth Clay. Smith knew the Fuller's Earth in greater detail than any other formation, for Cottage Crescent was built upon it and much of his canal passed through it]. This Clay or rather Clayey Marl is always found to accompany the upper Bed of the Bastard Freestone in the manner described in the sections annexed. By the openings which have been made into it at the Cottage Crescent & by the side of the Wells Road at 4½ Miles from Bath and the new Road from Bath to Bradford it does not appear to be more than   feet thick of a darkish blue colour & rather lamilated. A specimen which I tried did not effervesce with ascids [a basic test for limestone]. The most remarkable thing which distinguishes it from several beds of the same appearance is the Natrum Selinite or Rhomboidal Selinite which I have found imbed in it at the first two planes above described & the Revd. Mr   an engenious friend of mine has also found it in great quantities in the same bed near Bradford [-on-Avon].

No.8 *Yellow Clay & Clayey Stone &c.* This Stratum or rather Class of Stones [&] Clay alternating with one another seem to partake of the colour and quality of the Fuller's Earth which lays immediately under.

[No.] 9 *Fuller's Earth.* This very useful and highly prized Earth is found in great abundance in many of the wet sidelaying Lands near the Tops of the Hills about Bath it is never found far from that tier of springs which issue from the upper Stratum of Freestone and the place where it lays may be easily distinguished by the poverty of the surface which I have often observed to be some of the worst land in the neighbourhood of

Bath.

No.10 *Light blue Clay*. [Formations 10 and 11 are the Lower Fuller's Earth Clay]

No. 11 *Bastard Fuller's Earth*. The Bed of bastard Fuller's Earth which was found in sinking the Shafts and Cistern for the Caisson [Robert Weldon's ingenious but unsuccessful caisson lock on the canal at Combe Hay - described and illustrated in J Billingsley's *General View of the Agriculture of the County of Somerset* (1797), p.317., p1. xv] and also in the bottom of the place where the Caisson was built and which appears in different parts of the cutting thro' Blacklands Furlong Barnards and Sabins Tynings does not lay much above the under division of the Freestone or Bastard Freestone Rock in this neighbourhood.

No.12 *Lower Bed of Bastard Freestone* [the Inferior Oolite]. This class of Stones or division of the Freestone Grit is composed of several thick beds of diferent degrees of hardness and of diferent Qualitis the top bed which lays Immediately under the Clay is a Hard greyish Limestone full of Clayholes and generally incrusted with petrifactions from the hard water which filters thro' the incumbent Clay and this to such a degree as to cement the Rocks together so as to be seperated with great dificulty. This is comonly called by the Quarry men burnt stuff tho it has much more the appearance of Ice and in some places assumes the shape of Isciles which are generally hollow within with a drop of clear water at the end of each.

No.13 *Sand & Sandbars* [the Midford Sands]. This Stratum of Ferruginous Sand or Sandy Stone which in some places has beds in it hard enough for building is abt. 30 ft. thick and lays immediately under the Bastard Freestone is of a brownish yellow Colour very compact in the upper part with a little soft which calcarious matter between the joints the middle part is softer in veining with hard burs between and the joints of the sand & sides of the Burs are often deeply tinged with Feruginous matter. This part of the sand is damper than the top and tho firm enough to form Caves in without [word illegible] is not so close and firm as the top nor so hard as the bottom beds some of which cannot be cut with Steel. These beds have large open joints between them disposed in the same regular manner as was observed in the Freestones & Chalk and serve as the Channels for that water which is the abundant supply of the numerous springs issuing from the bottom of the sand.

No.14 *Light blue sandy stuff* [Formations 14 and 15 of this list are omitted in the 1799 list, where they are presumably included in the Blue Marl].

No.15 *Clay mixed with sandy particles & Ochre-balls.*

No.16 *Blue Marl.*

No.17 *Blue or grey Lias.*

No. 18 *White Lias*. This Stratum Is composed of thin Beds of fine grained stone imbeded in Clay in the same manner as the Blue Lias just described and partakes of the same qualities tho some of the Beds are nearly as white as Chalk and not much harder when first taken out of the Quarry - but when dug in the summer & properly dried makes excelent stone for building or paving Houses and is much used for both purposes in Somersetshlre and if well dressed looks very neat but some Sods are much to be preferred to others. This Stone is so very comon in Somersetshire and has been so long wrought that the Quarrymen know the exact Number of Beds and have assigned to each a name - the fowllowing are the common appelations about the Timsbury & Camerton Coa!works.

No. 19 *Black Marl* [the Rhaetic]. Tho' this stratum is well known in Somersetshire and its good effects as a Manure have been long felt in diferent parts of the Country yet the above term cannot give a Stranger a correct Idea of the substance tho, it may point out [its] properties.

No.20 *Red Ground* [the Keuper Marl]. This is the most bulky Stratum for Coal in Somersetshlre having been found in some places near 30 fathoms [55m] thick and tho it is nearly of the same colour throughout it differs matteria!ly in quality some parts of it being a sharp sand others a tenacious Clay some of a stony consistence & others a perfect flat beded Stone which may be taken up in large flags fit for building.

No.21 *Millstone* [the Dolomitic Conglomerate]. The Millstone seems to be lodged or imbeded in the upper part of the Stratum of Red ground which runs thro' this Country and which I conceive to be of an Irony Quality. A great part of Mendip is composed of Limestone Rocks the Fragments of which it should seem fell in the way of the Irony particles united with it and formed this uncommonly hard Cement or Stratum of concreted matter which about Mendip is called the Millstone and which is evidently composed of part Limestone and part Ironstone and which perhaps, if it was burnt & pulverized would form a good cement for building in water. How it comes to pass that this stone is not so thick and of a diferent form in the Measures which it should be found in about Camerton and other Coalworks as it is nearer to Mendip I am at a loss to account.

No.22 *Pennant Stone*. [As in the 1799 list, the Pennant Stone is placed above the Coal Measures although Smith well knew that in the collieries near High Littleton, where he had worked for several years, the Coal Measures are overlain directly by the red marls of the Trias. There are, of course, two series of Coal Measures in Northern Somerset, one above and one below the Pennant Grit]. This laminated Stone of a greyish colour and gritty Quality is found under the red Ground and generally divided from it by a Bed of yellow tough Clay - called by Colliers the tops of Cleeves.

No.23 *Greys*. [A local miners' term for hard carbonaceous grit of the Coal Measures].

No.24 *Iron Stone*.

No.25 *Clift*. [A local miners' term for hard, laminated, black, or grey shale with plant remains].

No. 26 *Coal*.

No. 27 *Coal*. Many Writers have taken great pains to examine into the Component particles of Coal in order to account for its formation and finding many vegitabie impressions in its concomitant Strata have thence judged it to be of vegitable origin and puzzled and confounded themselves and their readers with many unnecessary perplexities concerning it unless they could tell what formed Freestone Limestone Clay Ironstone or any other Mineral Body as well as Coal for there is not a doubt but they were all formed at the same time as the great Mass was formed of which Coal is no insignificant part not lying in heaps as many have imagined but regularly dispersed throughout such parts of the Globe as the Creator of all things thought fit to place them in.

[No.] 28 *Limestone*.

The 1799 list ended with the Coal. It is, therefore, interesting to see that in 1797 Smith correctly placed the Carboniferous Limestone below the Coal measures, although a few years later he was less certain of its position. He also knew nothing at this stage of the Old Red Sandstone (of the Devonian Period) beneath it, although it crops out only a few miles to the south-east, between Radstock and Shepton Mallet. He made no detailed observations on it until his visit to Wales in 1809-11. Then, he was able to note:

> the district of land which is well known by this name (Red Rab) in South Wales may now be distinctly traced through the borders of Herefordshire and Radnorshire into North Wales. It crosses the River Dee between Corven and Llangollen and goes out to sea

> somewhere about Conway. Its course between the place where it crosses the Vale of Llangollen and Conway may be expected to be along the S.W. side of the Vale of Clwyd, near to Ruthin, Denbigh and Bettws, and along the course of which gentlemen's seats and genteel houses are very numerous.

1797 list	1799 list
Omitted	Stratum 5 *Clay* (Probably of the Forest Marble series, as the position, above the Forest Marble, is wrong for the Bradford Clay).
Stratum 10 *Light blue Clay.*	Omitted. Probably included in *Bastard Fuller's Earth and Sundries*
Strata 15 and 16 *Clay mixed with sandy particles and Ochre–balls*	Omitted. Probably .included in the *Blue Marl.*
Stratum 24 *Iron Stone.*	Omitted. Probably included under *Grays*
Strata 26 and 27 *Coal.*	Only one stratum allotted.
Stratum 28 *Limestone.*	Omitted.

Douglas and Cox conclude:

> It is thus clear that the main details of the succession around Bath which Smith gave in 1799 had already been known to him for several years - probably since 1793 or 1794. From 1794 to 1799 he was occupied with the exacting duties of Resident Engineer to the Somerset Coal Canal Company, and his geological observations were necessarily confined to the formations excavated during the construction of the canal, and such exposures as he could examine between Bath and the canal, and on very occasional journeys along the Bath-Warminster road to see his friends, Thomas Davis of Longleat and the Rev. Benjamin Richardson, then living at Woolverton. It has often been pointed out that the 1799 list, like the present one, omits all the upper part of the Jurassic together with the Lower Greensand, the reason being that the Gault rests

> directly on Oxford Clay at the only place (near the Black Dog Inn, south of Standerwlck) where its outcrop crosses the Bath-Warminster road, and the exposures in the vicinity were insufficient to enable Smith to discriminate between the two clay formations. The Gault overstep is well seen at the present time in abandoned workings for Westbury Iron Ore near Bremeridge Farm, between Dilton Marsh and Penleigh, as demonstrated by Mr. G.A. Kellaway to the International Geological Congress party who visited the area recently. At the eastern end of these workings the Gault rests on Kimmeridge Clay, which itself overlies the iron ore of Upper Corallian age [part of the Upper Jurassic]. A little further to the west the Gault rests directly on the iron ore, and at the western end of the workings the ore has itself been cut out by the unconformity, and the Gault rests on Lower Calcareous Grit. Further west there is no trace at all of Corallian rocks. No doubt had the Westbury Iron Ore been worked in Smith's time, he would have made a detour from his customary route early in his investigations to study its geological position; this ore was, however, first worked in 1856.
>
> As events were to prove, Smith's 1799 list of formations was somewhat premature. From that year onwards, he was no longer tied to his canal work and had many more opportunities to explore the countryside around Bath and to travel to other parts of England. Such formations as the Bradford Clay, the Cornbrash, the Kellaways Rock, and the 'Clunch' [Oxford] Clay were soon discovered and assigned to their correct stratigraphical positions. The Corallian rocks and Kimmeridge Clay of western Wiltshire and the Lower Greensand of Seend also became known to him, although it was not until the earlier copies of his great map of 1815 had been printed and distributed that the succession of the Upper Jurassic and Lower Cretaceous formations was correctly unravelled.

The extremely wet weather of 1799 had been the cause of a number of serious landslides, in some cases carrying houses away with them. Springs were pouring into unstable clay. Smith was able to bring to bear his drainage skills in Bath and Batheaston. At Combegrove, near Bath, he found that all the buildings had been affected by rockfalls and landslides, and he expressed the fear that, within a few years, the whole area would succumb. However, by tunnelling into the hillside and intercepting the springs, he entirely prevented further damage. His reputation soon spread, and he was asked to apply his knowledge in Gloucestershire, the Isle of Purbeck, and Wiltshire. In this new direction of his career, he was strongly encouraged by the Chairman of the

Canal Company, Mr. Stephens of Camerton, and one of the best farmers in the Bath district, Mr. T. Crook of Tytherton. In the wet years, the clay on which most of the country's corn was grown remained too soggy, and the crop was poor. Smith was called in to improve the drainage and thus to ameliorate the yield. In dry years, the clay became desiccated, so he turned his skills to irrigation. During all this employment, which carried him far and wide, he enjoyed the opportunity to further his studies of local geology. In 1800, he coloured a geological map connecting the structure of the north of England with that of the south-west, showing quite accurately the whole Oolitic series across the country. This map was known to be in York Museum in 1831, but now seems lost. In the same year, he was invited to Mr. Crook's house to meet the famous Thomas William Coke of Holkham (later Earl of Leicester of Holkham), one of the first English agriculturalists, and to demonstrate his drainage techniques to him. Coke immediately asked him to his home, where there was much work for him to do. Smith travelled from Bath to Holkham on horseback, using Cary's one-sheet England map. On his return, he went across the Fens to Peterborough and Danbury, getting down from his horse from time to time to sketch sections of some of the hills, mark stone quarries and outcrops of rocks, and to fill his pockets with fossils.

During the following year, Smith's services were heavily in demand all over the country, even from as far away as Ireland. He visited mines in Cheshire and North Wales, Monmouthshire, Shropshire and Staffordshire, and mentioned in a letter to Richardson that he had been to the North of England and Scotland, so he was kept so busy that he hardly had time to put down all he was learning about what he thought of as a new science. He did, however, put together some ideas about a proposed publication dealing with the Earth's geology. It was headed:

> *Plan of the Work: To be divided into Two Parts.* The *First* should treat of the structure of the earth, or the general disposition of the most remarkable known strata, collected from the best authorities, and arranged according to the order discovered in England, and the *Second* should enter into the particulars of each stratum, with the fossils and minerals that have hitherto been discovered, with their connection and dependence one upon another. Though it is impossible for the labours of an individual ever to accomplish a thousandth part of what is proposed by this section; yet when a system is established which has Nature for its prototype, every one will be enabled to contribute his mite, and carry it on from time to time, till after ages may get a tolerable description of the habitable world.
>
> *Many* sections of the strata, in different directions, will be necessary to show their various inclinations. In the general section, each principal stratum should be numbered with progressive numbers, beginning at

> the eastern strata of the kingdom; or, till that can be accurately ascertained, at some stratum that forms a grand feature therein. As for instance, the chalk which I would call No. 1; and those lesser strata which are contained within it, or generally attached to it, or form any subdivisions therein, I would call 1a, 1b, 1c., &c. If any thin stratum should be omitted, or a new one discovered, it may be brought into those numbers, by making it 1aa, &c.
>
> After the general section of a country or district, should follow a large section of each stratum, with its concomitant small strata; with drawings and descriptions of such peculiarities as the principal stratum, or those connected with it, are found to contain; whether the exuviae of marine animals, vegetable impressions, or fossil wood, coal, and metal of every description.
>
> The same numbers which refer to the section, may refer to an explanation of the chemical properties of each substance, so far as discovered. This may be placed at the end of a book, or make a separate volume where those properties may be more minutely examined than can consistently be done in the body of the work, which is intended to form a true representation of the order of Nature, with no more digressions from the main subject than are absolutely necessary to make it intelligible. Plates should be bound up at the end of each volume, in a peculiar manner; these, as well as the strata, to make them more striking, should be coloured.
>
> The Second Section of the work may be divided into chapters, each stratum making a chapter or division, to which its name in conspicuous characters should stand as a title. The names of particular substances described in this division should also appear conspicuous and striking as well as the places they are found at, or near to; and a more particular section will accompany each part of the work, with a map divided into squares, or published in parts, which may be united together, and form a complete map and general section on a large scale.
>
> The chemical part, which refers to the other by the numbers, may be arranged under the heads Iron, Coal, Limestone, &c. By this means those veins which lie very distant from each other, will admit of an easier comparison. This should form a summary of the more useful minerals.

His great friend, the Rev. Benjamin Richardson, brought to his attention that somebody else might beat him to publication of ideas that should rightfully be credited to him. He drew up in haste a document entitled *Prospectus of a Work / entitled Accurate Delineations / and Descriptions / of the / Natural*

Order / of the various / Strata / that are found in different parts of / England and Wales / with Practical Observations / thereon. /By William Smith, / Land-surveyor and Drainer, / and member of the Bath Agricultural Society. He wanted to put forward a review of his observations and to demonstrate their practical applications. He wrote:

> The Philosopher may derive an inexhaustible fund of valuable information. The miner may learn more readily, as well as more certainly, to trace the course of his ore; and, while his ideas are extended a curiosity will naturally be excited, that may pave the way to new and unthought-of discoveries. The various artists employed in building, from the humble Mortar-maker to the enlightened Architect, must all be interested in a method of discovering sand, clay, stone, slate, and other materials, and of selecting with certainty such as are best. Fullers, Founders, Glass-makers, etc., will learn where to send for earths and sands of the qualities best suited to their respective purposes; and sources of supply will, probably, be opened in places of which they now entertain no idea. Chemists, Colour-men, Vitriol, Alum, and Saltmakers, will learn how to trace the materials they have occasion for; and will be enabled frequently to obtain, at once, the different advantages of more convenient situations, smaller expense, and an improved quality. The Canal Engineer will be enabled to choose his stratum, find the most appropriate materials, avoid slippery ground, or remedy the evil. The Building Contractor may also form his estimates with more certainty to himself, and more satisfaction to his employer, by the experience he has had, and the observations that he will be lead to make on similar works in a like stratum. Brick-makers, Potters, and others, are also interested in a knowledge of the correct Theory of those materials which furnish their sole employment. Indeed, there are but few of the most necessary occupations of life, that may not derive from this Work some useful hint or improvement.
>
> The discovery of this regularity in the process of Nature, led the author to a complete knowledge of all springs, and the Drainage of Wet lands, which he is now practising in different parts of the kingdom, in the fullest confidence of being able to effect a complete cure on the most difficult subject of experiment.

He prepared;

> a correct map of the strata, describing the general course and width of each stratum on the surface, accompanied by a general section, showing their proportion, dip and direction. The maps and sections,

> to make them more striking and just representations of nature, will all be given in the proper colours.

He concluded his prospectus, issued from Mitford (Midford) and dated 1 June, 1801 as follows:

> to attempt a complete history of all the minutiae of strata would be an endless labour; for a long life devoted to such a pursuit must be inadequate to the purpose considering the immense variety which is found in this little island. But should the present essay meet with that liberal patronage from the public which the author has reason to expect, it is his intention, in a future work, to give a particular description of the numerous animal remains and vegetable impressions found in each stratum, with an accurate detail of every characteristic mark that has led him to these discoveries.

The prospectus was circulated widely, and a small uncoloured map, dated 1801 and published by Debrett of Piccadilly, was sent to the engraver. It aroused great interest, as people became aware of its existence and potential utility. Smith's friend Richardson endorsed Debrett's suggestion that an edition of the work be produced in Latin, the international language of science at the time, so that interested parties across Europe could benefit from it, and to prevent the French, for example, from pirating it. This map, together with Smith's earlier one of 1799, was presented to the Geological Society in 1831. As we shall see, the work itself was never published.

In 1801, the Rev. Richard Warner, Curate of St. James's in Bath, (who lived above and behind Smith's cottage at Tucking Mill), published his *History of Bath*. In a chapter entitled *On the Mineralogy and Fossilogy of the Environs of Bath,* he states:

> The mineralogical peculiarities of this district, indeed, are so numerous, that it would be inconsistent in a work like the present to descend to a minute investigation of them; we must, therefore, content ourselves with giving a general view of the strata which compose the surrounding hills, and their fossilogical contents, referring the reader for a more scientific and particular account of them to a work written expressly on the subject, by the very ingenious Mr. Smith, of Midford, near Bath, which, we understand, will shortly be given to the world; and which will contain the valuable results of a patient, long, and indefatigable attention to the mineralogy of the country around Bath.

This was the first public account of Smith's work. Warner goes on to give a detailed account of the sequence of the strata, using names given to some of them by Smith, without further acknowledgement of him. It seems surprising that there is no record of any protest by Smith. Later on, he was keen to ensure that he received full credit for his work.

In the summer of 1801, Smith attended the Woburn Sheepshearing. Such large agricultural meetings, also held at Holkham each June, were attended by upwards of 300 landed gentry and farmers and lasted four days. There were exhibitions of sheep and cattle, ploughing competitions, visits to neighbouring farms and sumptuous dinners provided by the hosts. Here Smith first met Sir Joseph Banks, President of the Royal Society. Banks showed enthusiasm for Smith's ideas for a geological map of England and Wales, and encouraged him to complete it. To accompany the map, Smith suggested the book, for which he had already issued a prospectus, entitled *Accurate Delineations and Descriptions of the Natural Order of the Various Strata That are Found in Different Parts of England and Wales*.

In the late summer or early autumn, Smith journeyed to the North of England and into Scotland. The knowledge he gained from observation of the geology added considerably to the detail and accuracy of the earliest surviving of his maps, dated 1801. It is based on a map of England and Wales on a scale of about thirty-seven miles to one inch, taken from *A General Atlas of the World* published in London by Robert Wilkinson in 1794. It is entitled *General Map of STRATA found in ENGLAND & WALES by William Smith Surveyor 1801.* There is no index to the colouring, but eight strata are identified: Chalk in green, Coral Rag ('Sand of Portland Rock') and Carstone in purple, Oxford Clay in pale grey, Oolite in yellow, Lias in dull blue, the New Red Sandstone in light red, Magnesian and Carboniferous Limestone in bright blue, and a miscellany of pre-Carboniferous rocks, all of which Smith thought of as 'Red Rab' (Old Red Sandstone) in reddish-brown. This map also graces the library of the Geological Society of London.

Coke, later that same year, introduced Smith to Francis, Duke of Bedford, by whom he was given considerable drainage and irrigation work on his estate at Woburn. Elkington, a Warwickshire farmer who had originated a drainage system for a range of boggy grounds, and who had received a grant of £1000 from Parliament to divulge his method, had attempted in 1795 to drain the bog on Prisley Farm, near Flitwick, Westoning and Tingrith on the Woburn Estate. This bog had been selected as a trial for Elkington's process by the Board of Agriculture. He failed due to lack of experience. Smith took over and applied his own scheme based on his knowledge of geology. He succeeded in turning 9 acres (3·6 hectares) of what had seemed a hopeless case of worthless land into valuable meadows, by conducting a running stream over the surface. He wrote later that he had had to take up all Elkington's drains and added, 'Hence it appears necessary for the designer of plans of irrigation to be fully master of the art of draining, which

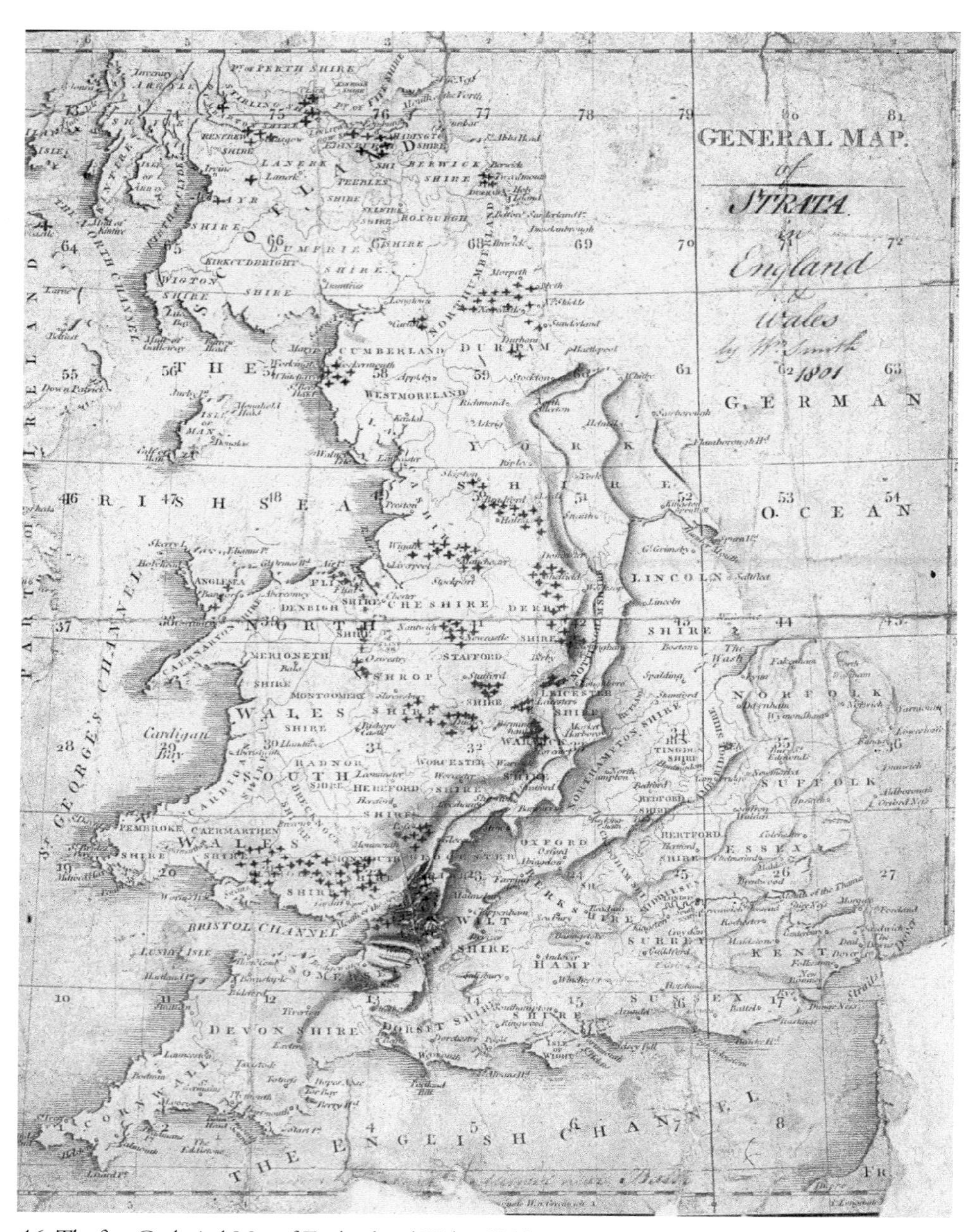

16. The first Geological Map of England and Wales, 1801.

17. Facsimile, very slightly reduced, of the first page of Smith's prospectus of 1801.

An original before Title

PROSPECTUS OF A WORK,
ENTITLED,
ACCURATE DELINEATIONS
AND
DESCRIPTIONS
OF THE
NATURAL ORDER
OF THE VARIOUS
STRATA
THAT ARE FOUND IN DIFFERENT PARTS OF
ENGLAND AND WALES:
WITH
PRACTICAL OBSERVATIONS
THEREON.

BY WILLIAM SMITH,
LAND-SURVEYOR AND DRAINER,
AND MEMBER OF THE BATH AGRICULTURAL SOCIETY.

" All Nature is but Art unknown to thee;
All Chance, Direction which thou canst not see;
All Discord, Harmony not understood;
All partial Evil, universal Good." POPE.

IT cannot be necessary to use many words in pointing out, to persons of judgment and discrimination, the uses to which discoveries of the nature above alluded to, may be applied; for what can be of greater importance in human science, than a Complete Theory of the Soil, which man is under a divine injunction to cultivate and replenish, that he may derive from that labour his daily subsistence? As on this particular province, therefore, depends the acquisition, not only of his own conveniencies and comforts, but those of every other creature that has been subjected to his will, too

Printed by B. M'Millan, Bow-street, Covent-garden.

Presented to the Geological Society Feby 18th 1831 by Wm Smith

cannot be well understood but by a knowledge of the strata.' For 'various improvements in the irrigation of boggy land and rendering it valuable' he was awarded a silver medal by the Society for the Encouragement of Arts, Manufacture and Commerce. It was presented to him by the Duke of Norfolk, the Society's President, at the Adelphi (London) on 28 May, 1805.

Smith submitted an account to the Society of how he had gone about the work. It was entitled *Mode of improving Boggy Land*:

> The whole surface of the boggy ground was pared with a breast-plough, and the peaty matter thrown together in ridges, like common high-ploughed land, with a ridge like a head-ridge, at one end of each

set of ridges. Each ridge has a cut or channel for water on the top, and a drain in the furrow or hollow between it and the next ridge. The head-ridge has a larger channel for water on its top, which supplies all the other ridges with water, and this main ridge is itself supplied by its connexion with a larger channel or feeder, which first conveys the water out of the common brook-course into the meadow.

The furrow between each head-ridge and the ends of the beds has a larger drain, into which all the channels of drains in the furrows discharge their water, and which is by this main drain carried into the brook-course again. Thus the water is diverted out of its usual channel, only to float over the surface of the land, and run into that channel again lower down.

To get the water high enough to swim over the surface of any piece of ground, it is generally necessary to make a dam in the original channel, to pen up the water, till it rises to the surface, or near it, and convey it along a channel which shall have less fall than the brook, until it can be got out upon the surface. The length of such conduit or drain must therefore depend upon the fall in the lands which lie parallel to the original channel of the water; and the quantity of land that can be covered with water, depends upon the distance between the proposed new channel and the old ones.

And, to perform this business in the most methodical manner, it is necessary to new model the surface, otherwise the water (which will always find its level) would lie too deep, or move too slowly over the low places in the ground, and thereby injure the grasses by a redundancy of water, while all the high parts of the ground would appear like little islands above the surface of the water, and consequently receive no benefit from such an imperfect system of irrigation.

Where these inequalities of surface are large and numerous, it will be attended with much more expense to make such land into a regular form for floating, on account of the great expense of wheeling the earth from the hills to the hollows. In these cases, it is necessary (in order to avoid expense) to adopt an irregular method of floating: by taking advantage of such irregularities of surface, a meadow may often be floated at a quarter of the expense required to put it into a regular form, and this method is found to answer the purpose very well, if the works are properly laid out with the spirit level. When the fall of water is ascertained, the form of the ground is the next thing to be attended to; if there are no natural declivities in the surface, down which the water may run from the overflowings of a cut on the summit into a drain in the hollows, so that the water may keep constantly running down such slopes by a regular current, which prevents a diminution on the ridges and a quick discharge in the lower drain; to avoid an accumulation in the furrows, it must be made with good slopes and plenty of drains; these, with a constant supply of water in the winter, are the most essential parts of a water-meadow. The water must be constantly kept moving over the surface, and the practice proves, that where the water moves the quickest, there is always the most grass.

And, as the water must be constantly running off the land, it follows that it must be constantly running on, to keep every part of the surface properly supplied; and this requires a much greater quantity of water than is commonly imagined by those, who are wholly unacquainted with the practice of irrigation. In fact, every good water-meadow should be formed so that it may be said to be nothing but a wide extended channel for the water, no part of which should be too deep to prevent the points of the grass from appearing above its surface, consequently the water cannot be seen when the grass begins to grow. Yet it will still find its way between the shoots, and nourish the grass without bearing it down, or excluding it from the benefit of the air and sun: this is a state, in which the grasses of a water-meadow increase very rapidly: in this state, no water can be seen in any part of a meadow, but in the cuts which bring it on and drains that take it off; the motion down the slopes is only perceptible where it runs off the upper cut and in the lower drain; in the still more perfect parts, when the grass has got a considerable shoot, even this part of its motion is not perceptible; and a well-regulated meadow, in the spring, cannot be known to be in a state of irrigation without walking into it. The water running among the shoots, soon becomes perceptible to the foot which proves that there is no inconsiderable quantity running down the slopes, though its motion upon that part cannot be seen.

It is therefore one of the fundamental principles of irrigation, to keep the water moving, and that in such well regulated quantities as shall neither be too great nor too little; for both of the extremes are alike unfriendly to vegetation; but I believe there is much more mischief done to a water meadow by giving it too little, than too much water, and the greater the supply the less nicety is required in the adjustment, if the meadow is so laid out as to prevent its accumulation in any part thereof. But where the quantity of water is small, it is necessary to be very nice in the distribution of it, in order to receive the full benefit of the stream upon as much land as it is capable of floating.

Here again we must not run into extremes, and try to get the water over too much land at a time, and thereby prevent the grass from receiving the full benefit of a quantity of water which is capable of giving it a good soaking: what that quantity is, will be best determined by practice, for some ground requires much more water than others. In case of a short supply of water, which is extended to the improvement of as much land as it is capable of covering, according to the best principles of irrigation, it will be better to unite all the water upon such a portion of the work as practice shall prove it capable of covering well, and to let that part have the full benefit of the water as long at a time as is necessary to give a good soaking, or as long as it may be kept off the other parts without injury.

In some meadows, after they have had a complete soaking, which has saturated the soil, and the grass has thickened upon the surface, vegetation will not be retarded for some time for want of water, and those parts which were forced the most in the autumn, will require the least in the spring. It will therefore be always advisable, on account of the water and a succession of grass, to get some part of the water-meadow as forward as possible in the autumn, that that part may be dried and fed the first in the spring, while all the water is employed in forcing on those other parts of the meadow which were neglected in the autumn. 'By a prudent management of the water in uniting its vegetative powers upon those pieces of meadow which are disposed to produce the earliest vegetation in the spring, and so on in succession, from the earliest to the latest pieces of ground, or those which can be made so; a regular succession of grasses might be obtained, which would be much better than trying to get the whole alike, especially, if the quantity in one person's possession be very considerable, and his quantity of water likely to fail or barely to suffice for the purpose.

This method of using the water in succession upon portions of the meadow, which practice shall prove it capable of covering at one time, will be applicable to most meadows; for there are few, that are well formed, that have too much water, especially in the winter, or where there are any mills or navigations; I have generally observed that the best meadows upon the large streams, are those which have the most water and the best falls.

Account of the nine acres of Water Meadow, on Prisley Farm near Fletwick, Westoning, and Tingrith in Bedfordshire.

As the quantity of water is sometimes insufficient to float the whole of this meadow at once, it has been contrived to be divided into three parts, by means of two large hatches, within the meadow. Each of these principle divisions may again be divided into still smaller parts, by putting a common hatch or board made to the shape of either of the main feeders, which will stop the water out of any part, and force so much the more upon that which is intended to be floated. These contrivances are often necessary on account of the great scarcity of water, and also for the purpose of employing all the water upon any one part of the meadow, while the grass is feeding off the other; and (if the levels will admit of it) something like this ought to be done in every good water-meadow, for it is not merely the elevated or high-ridged form of the surface, which constitutes a good water-meadow, but such a disposition of the parts as is best calculated for the general purposes to which the land, the water, or its produce, may be most advantageously applied. The three parts of this meadow are upon two different levels, so that the drawing of either of the hatches before mentioned lays all the high part dry, and puts either the North or the South part of the lower level afloat at the same time. By keeping down one of those hatches and opening the other, all the water may be turned either upon the North or the South part of the low level, as occasion may require; or if both the hatches be shut down, the whole of the water may be used upon the high level, or two first sets of beds.

If there is more water than is sufficient to float either of the three parts separately, either of the two regulating hatches may be fixed at such a height as to use the remainder on the upper level; or the high level of the meadow may be made to receive its full quantity of water, and an opening be left under one or both of the hatches, so as to distribute the remainder of the water on either of the parts of the lower level, wherever it may be wanting; or the whole of the water may be used upon one of the lower levels, by adjusting the hatch so that that part shall have sufficient water, and drawing up the other high enough to discharge the surplus; or, if one part is floating, and neither of the other pieces are in want of water, any overplus may be turned down the waste ditch which divides the meadow from the upland, by drawing the outside or main hatch, high enough to discharge such surplus water under it.

The water is capable of all these variations, but there will seldom be any occasion for turning any water to waste, as it may generally be all employed upon the meadow or upon a third of it. If the other two parts should be in use, it will be found most advisable to feed only one part of such meadow at a time, as the other two thirds might then be floating alternately. When that third has been fed off, the most forward of the other two may then be laid dry for feeding, and the new-fed part floated in its stead. By this plan of feeding one-third at a time, and keeping the other two thirds afloat at the same time, either together or separately, according to the quantity of water, the water will always be constantly employed from the first commencement of floating to the conclusion of the feeding and floating after it; when the whole may be shut up together for mowing.

The spring floating may be continued at intervals, (if the water be not foul) till the grass has gained a considerable height, but it must only be put on for a day or two at a time to cool the ground, and keep the grass growing. This management, if it be well conducted, will be of great service in forwarding the crop and increasing the bulk; the ground will also be the cooler and better for it when the crop comes off, consequently, it will occasion the after-grass to grow so much the quicker. No time should be lost in putting on the water immediately after the hay has been removed; or, as soon as one-third of the meadow can be cleared, the water should be immediately put upon that part till it is pretty well soaked, and then upon the other parts, in their turns, as soon as they are cleared. Great care should be taken both in feeding and taking off the hay, that it be done with a view of clearing that part first, where the water can be first applied to the purpose of producing another crop. The water should never run to waste but in the height of summer, when the grass may be high enough to form a thick cover to the ground, and keep it cool and moist enough for the purposes of vegetation without the aid of water; and also at the end of summer or autumn, when, if the meadows are fed with sheep, there may be some danger of rotting them by using the water at this time of the year. It will appear to those who acquainted with the management of Wiltshire water-meadows (by the account annexed, which I received from his Grace the Duke of Bedford, and which states the quantity of grass cut and the time of feeding the meadow), that the grass was begun to be fed off before it was fit; and from the long time that the sheep were kept upon the ground during the months of February, March, and April, there was much of the water wasted, which should have hourly been employed at the most prolifick season. Experience proves, that there is no danger of getting the grasses too strong upon the ground at this early season, and that crops which are six or seven inches high, and apparently too coarse and high for a bullock to feed, are eaten with the most eagerness by sheep in the spring; and those parts where the grass is thickest and most luxuriant are always fed the closest, and sought after with greatest avidity. This being contrary to the grazing habits of all animals which graze upon dry pastures, where they give a decided preference to short and sweet herbage, may lead many persons to think that the grass of a water-meadow may be too high and luxuriant for sheep; but experience has proved, that such long grass is neither unfriendly nor unsavoury to them; and we know, that the grass always grows the fastest when it has gained considerable height and strength. It will also thicken at the bottom, and the roots will get much stronger hold in the ground, and consequently will not be subject to feel the want of water so soon during the time of feeding, and be able to make a much stronger shoot as soon as it is shut up again, and the water restored to it. The greatest crop will also be of the best quality both in grass and hay, and will always be fed much closer and evener than in those places where the floating has been any ways deficient. The drowner, as he is generally called, or the man who has the superintendance of water-meadows, should therefore endeavour to make every part of the crop as uniform as possible; for no meadow can be said to be complete till that is accomplished, and a good eye may easily discover the management of a meadow by the crop upon the ground, whether it be in the spring, summer, or autumn: for, if the grass appear patchy, or of different sorts and colours, there can be no doubt but that the water has been partially applied. The different shades of the ground after close feeding and mowing, will also show the parts which have had the most water, and where it has been deficient.

Workmen who have been accustomed to the mowing [of] such crops, can also tell all those parts by the different cut of the grass. Much of the perfection of a water-meadow also depends upon the care and pride which the drowner takes, in doing his work well. It would therefore be very advisable not to change those men too often, but to keep the water-meadow constantly under the care of the same workman, so long as he manages it well; and no one should ever alter the water but him who has the constant care of attending it. Water-meadows will never be brought to perfection in any country, till the proprietors and managers of them shall take a pride in doing them well, and strive to rival each other in excellence. Land-owners and agricultural societies should therefore offer premiums for the greatest produce that can be obtained from a given quantity of water-meadow, and a smaller premium to the drowner or managing man. This would excite emulation, and create a conversation and rival spirit of industry,

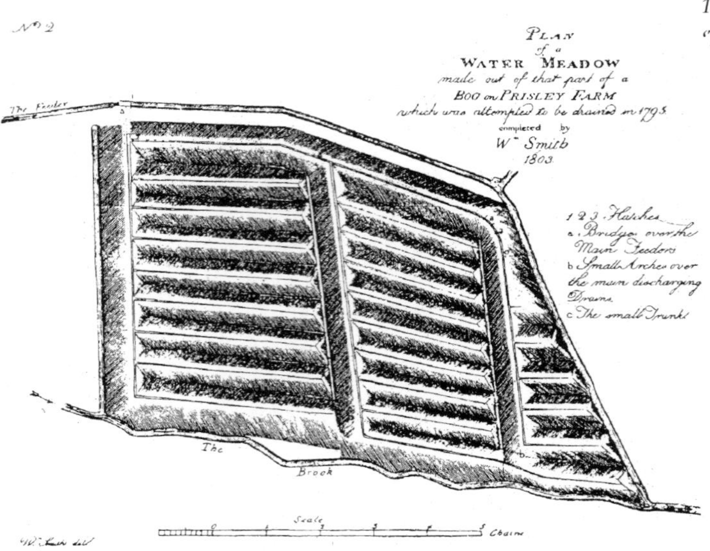

18. A plate in Smith's 'Treatise on Irrigation'.

and attention to a pursuit which many might not otherwise have thought about; as the crops of water-meadows are much more at the command of the farmer and less subject to blight, drought, or uncertainty of season, than any other crop which he cultivates; this would be a fair subject of competition in the skill of the managers, and the premium should not be determined by the produce of a single crop, but by the aggregate produce of the whole year, taken in spring-feed, hay, and autumn-feed.

Account delivered to Mr. Smith, by order of his Grace the Duke of Bedford, of the produce of nine acres from Prisley Water Meadow, made out of a Bog.

1803.

March 29th.	Stocked it with 12 score of sheep, kept them three weeks.
April 16th.	Shut it up for hay.
June 23rd.	Cut the first crop of hay, supposed to be above two tons per acre.
August 20th.	Cut the second crop, supposed to be one and a half ton per acre.
September 16th.	Stocked it with four score of fat sheep, three weeks; after that it was pastured with lean bullocks, as long and as often as they could find food.

1804.

February 27th.	Stocked it with eight score and four lamb-hogs.
April 28th.	They have now been nine weeks. This is more than eighteen sheep to an acre for nine weeks. It had more and better water this last winter than the winter before, but from our want of grass upon the farm, we have eaten it longer than we should have done.
June 21st.	Began cutting the first crop of hay, which is a greater quantity than the year before, and a larger proportion of the best grasses.

N.B. At the Woburn sheep-shearing in June, 1805, the above meadow was examined by the Secretary of the Society, when the quantity of the grass upon it was not only found to be great, but the kinds of grass it produced in general, excellent in quality, and apparently, on comparison, to improve every year.

Reference to the annexed Plan of the six acres of Water-Meadow, on Prisley Farm.

1. The main hatch, which, when closed, occasions the water that is to irrigate the meadow, to flow into the feeder which fills the highest cuts, made upon the first eight ridges, from which cuts it gently glides down the slopes into the eight drains, which unite and discharge themselves under the arch at b.

2. The second hatch, which regulates the water for the ten ridges in the second division of the meadow.

3. The third hatch, which regulates the water for the five ridges in the third or lowest division of the meadow, from whence it falls into the old course of the brook.

CERTIFICATE

I DO certify that Mr. William Smith, land-surveyor and drainer, from Bath, and now of Buckingham-street, London, was employed by the Duke of Bedford, to improve part of one of his farms, in the parish of Flitwick, in Bedfordshire, called Prisley Bog. That two pieces thereof, one containing about five, and the other about six acres, were in the year 1803 naked pieces of bog, (in the same state that they were left, after Mr. Elkington's ineffectual attempt to drain them in the year 1795), and were wholly unproductive. That Mr. Smith planned, and entirely directed the improvement of these two pieces of land, by forming them into most complete water-meadows, a correct plan of one of which (viz. the six acres) is annexed. He has caused to be engraved also, the plan of another meadow on the same bog, containing nine acres, which he irrigated by direction of the late Duke of Bedford, in the year 1802. That these three meadows are done in the most complete manner, with many improvements, superior to any meadows which I have seen or read of; and the general improvement, both in the kind of herbage and quantity thereof, in the last summer and previous spring, were astonishingly great. Witness my hand,

JOHN FAREY.
12, Upper Crown-street, Westminster,
20th May, 1805.

The Duke also gave Smith encouragement and assistance in developing his geological research. In January 1802, Smith undertook, at the Duke's expense, an expedition to the edge of the chalk hills south of Woburn, to determine the true succession of the strata. His object was to assess the best agricultural use to which the land might be put, and to see if it could be improved. On this journey he was accompanied by the Duke's land-steward, John Farey, with whom he later developed a close friendship, and Benjamin Bevan of Leighton Buzzard (Leighton Beau-Desert). As they approached the foot of the hills, Smith forecast that they would find sharks' teeth. They very quickly came upon six, very similar to ones he had seen from chalk-pits near Warminster, some 100 miles to the south-west. In a letter to his friend the Rev. Richardson, Smith tells him of the fossils he has found, in particular the 'St. Cuthbert's Beads' (columnar joints of *Crinoidea*) from the Mendips and of the strata he identified on his expedition with Farey and Bevan. They were looking for coral and other limestones between the sand and the chalk. Although they did not find the strata, they did come across pieces of these rocks in the alluvial gravel. They also identified Greensand, Gault Clay, Carstone (brown iron-bearing sandstone, in which the grains are cemented by limonite) and White Sand. They noted the chemical and visual changes that had occurred where faults had brought two different strata together.

The Duke's interest in Smith's geological pursuits grew and he authorised a collection of fossils from all around Britain to be begun. They were to be arranged in a discrete room at Woburn in their order of stratification, and the Duke intended to institute chemical examination of them. It was therefore a tragic blow to Smith to lose this sponsorship through the sudden untimely death of his benefactor. The Duke was buried on 12th March, 1802, the very day that Smith was to have had a second meeting with him to discuss the collection. Smith's nephew, John Phillips, says in his *Memoirs of William Smith*:

> The unexpected death of the Duke of Bedford was mourned as a public loss; on Mr. Smith it fell with the weight of a private affliction. Admitted by this truly noble person, 'who valued men much more for their worth than their titles,' to unrestrained and friendly intercourse, he had been successful in convincing him of the real value of that scientific agriculture which his Grace wished to advance, of a thorough and practical knowledge of the strata on whose properties so much of the quality of the superjacent soil depends. He had been invited to explain fully the scientific objects which he sought to accomplish, the progress which he had made, the means which he possessed, and the assistance which he needed, for completing his gigantic task. He spoke to a congenial spirit, one who 'though born in such a high degree,' was an honest enthusiast like himself, and had already thrown all the weight of his rank, intelligence and fortune into the schemes of agricultural improvement, which then radiated throughout the kingdom, from Woburn and Holkham. He had found powerful patronage at the very moment when it was most needed, at the time when the public importance of his past Labours was becoming manifest to the world, and the fearful magnitude of the problem to which he had devoted his energies began to strike even his resolute heart with dismay. From this dread the Duke's kindness had relieved him. 'I considered,' says he in a MS. of this period, 'my last interview with his Grace as one of the most auspicious periods of my life. The plan which he had formed for making himself and others acquainted with the nature of my pursuits was just such as I wished to carry into effect. I had more to expect from his Grace than from all other men in the kingdom.'
>
> The effect of the sudden reverse of all these hopes was to delay, indefinitely, the publication of the work announced by Debrett in the form of Smith's prospectus, until the misfortunes of that enterprising bookseller put a stop to the project altogether.

However, Duke Francis's brother (his heir, Russell) continued to support Smith with favour and assistance, and the project of fitting up a geological collection under Smith's direction was not entirely abandoned.

Towards the end of April 1802, Smith was staying at the George Inn, Woburn, and John Farey spent a couple of days with him. He copied the lines of strata he had plotted on four sheets of Cary's large map of England (five miles to the inch) which included the environs of the estate. Farey also helped Smith to correct some of the lines of the Chalk they had seen together to the south of Woburn. He also assisted him in emending and colouring those of the Cornbrash (a limestone so named by Smith because corn grew well on the soil above it). Entries in Smith's diary for the following month show him using his notes to add data to this map and a smaller one of Cary's on a scale of fifteen miles to the inch. After considering the landscape, the depth of wells, pits and mineral springs, he concluded that his belief up to that time that the Chalk crossed the Thames at Gravesend was wrong and that it went out under the English Channel at Beachy Head.

John Farey was discharged from his position by the new Duke of Bedford and obliged to set himself up in London as a 'mineralogical surveyor'. In this, what he had learned from Smith stood him in good stead and they remained good friends. When, later, they were both living in London, Smith often called on him to apprise him of his latest observations. Farey contributed a large number of articles to various scientific journals, frequently acknowledging Smith's work. His papers contain the earliest published outline of the main principles discovered by Smith. In his *New Light on William Smith and his Work* (1942), L.R. Cox says of Farey:

> It is obvious that in writing [these papers] he had no wish to deprive Smith of the credit for his discoveries. He was, in fact, always most scrupulous in making every acknowledgement to Smith, and a few years later was to become Smith's most outspoken protagonist. Smith, however, was furious when copies of [Rees's New] *Cyclopaedia* articles were sent to him by Farey in August 1807, accompanied by a letter in which Farey trusted that Smith would not see reason to disapprove of the manner in which his unpublished discoveries had been mentioned, and hoped that his action would have the effect of exciting such a call for the publication of Smith's work as to reward him amply for putting them to press. Farey went on to explain that, in consequence of a joint request from the Board of Agriculture (whose County Reports were passing through a new edition) and Sir Joseph Banks, he had undertaken to make a survey of the county of Derbyshire, in which he was to combine as much of the knowledge that Mr. Smith had imparted to him respecting the stratification of the Island with the enquiries usually made by the Reporters for the Board of Agriculture. Farey further suggested that he would be saved unnecessary travel and expense if Smith would furnish him with the lines of strata which he had already ascertained and inserted in his large county map of Derbyshire. To this rather presumptuous request Smith sent a blank refusal. His feelings found relief in letters to Sir John Sinclair (President of the Board of Agriculture), and to his old friends Richardson, Townsend and Crawshay, pointing out that he himself (rather than a 'scientific pilferer', to whom he had chanced to

> communicate his ideas in conversation), had the first claim to be employed by the Board in the capacity mentioned. Sir John Sinclair's reply was to the effect that Farey had been engaged to undertake an Agricultural Survey of Derbyshire according to the plan laid down by the Board, and would have to attend to the subject of soil and minerals whether he had discussed these matters with Smith or not. Smith had already been asked to draw up an abstract of his own discoveries for the consideration of the Board, which might then be induced to take further action regarding their publication. Until Smith had produced the requested abstract, nothing could be done for him.
>
> The results of Farey's survey were embodied in his notable report entitled *General View of the Agriculture of Derbyshire*, which appeared in two volumes published respectively in 1811 and 1813. In the first volume, ten pages are devoted to a short account of Smith's discoveries and a list is given of the strata present in the south of England. This account closes with the expression of the sincere hope that such a desire may speedily be excited for the publication of that Gentleman's [Smith's] valuable Maps and Papers, and descriptions of his Fossils, illustrative of the British Strata, as would induce him to lay by his professional engagements in order to publish them, or which should dispose him to give them up to such persons as would speedily bring them before the public.

Another small map, measuring 16½ by 10 inches, probably constructed in 1802 or 1803, was entitled *Map of STRATA in ENGLAND & WALES and part of SCOTLAND with all the collieries and mines accurately delineated by Wm. Smith Landsurveyor.* It is incomplete, but shows Tertiaries in brown, Chalk (to which particular attention has been paid) in green, and Lias confused with Carboniferous Limestone in blue. The New Red Sandstone is coloured reddish brown and the Old Red Sandstone has been depicted with a faint red wash. It is thought that this last was added at a later stage. At around this time, Smith increased his fees to two guineas (£2.10) a day, plus travelling expenses, because of the numerous simultaneous demands on his skills. However, he spent so much on his obsession with his geological map, because he felt it was a public service, that he was never substantially in funds. Smith was able to go to the large annual meetings, coinciding with the June sheepshearing season, which were attended by landowners and distinguished foreigners, to whom he showed his maps and talked about the economic value of his geological studies. Some of these maps are still in existence.

From 1802 to 1805, though still living at Tucking Mill, Smith set up in partnership as land-surveyors with Jeremiah Cruse at No. 3 Trim Street, Bath.

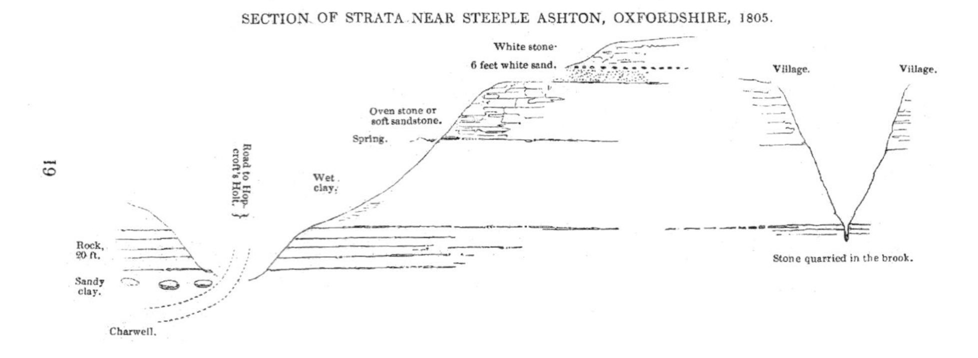

19. Smith's Section of the Strata near Steeple Ashton, Oxfordshire, 1805.

He rented the house next door (No. 2) in which to house his fossil collection. He was visited there on 8 August by William Reynolds of Coalbrookdale, the birthplace of the Industrial Revolution, and other eminent persons. Reynolds produced from his pocket a copy of the Table of Strata, drawn up in 1799, and stated that he knew that copies had been sent to both the East and West Indies. Since these are both predominantly volcanic, rather than sedimentary regions, it would not be inappropriate to wonder why! Rather than having to endure rivalry in the field of his discoveries, Smith enjoyed the fullest co-operation from his friends and acquaintances. Joseph Townsend gave him a series of his own drawings of fossils he had collected or seen elsewhere, to be included in Smith's new book. He enjoyed practical support from Coke of Holkham, the new Duke of Bedford, Sir Joseph Banks and Richard Crawshay, the proprietor of the Cyfarthfa Ironworks near Merthyr Tydfil. Crawshay advanced money for the purpose of publishing Smith's researches. The Duke brought Smith's work to the attention of Arthur Young, then Secretary to the Board of Agriculture, who invited him to explain to the Board the progress he had made in the drawing up of geological maps and their application to agriculture.

Over the next ten years, Smith was constantly employed on different projects from Wales to Kent and Norfolk to Yorkshire, and had little time for writing. He only published one book, and that not really related to geology. The title page of this read:

> *Observations / on the Utility, Form and Management / of Water Meadows, / and the Draining and Irrigating / of Peat Bogs, / with / An Account of Prisley Bog, / and other / Extraordinary Improvements, / conducted for / His Grace the Duke of Bedford, / Thomas William Coke, Esq., M.P. / and others; / By William Smith, / Engineer and Mineralogist. / Norwich*: Printed for John Harding, 66, St. James's Street, / London, / 1806.

It appeared that year, timed to coincide with the Holkham Sheepshearing (21-25 June). It was largely an explanation of how he had gone about draining the bog on Prisley Farm in 1803, which he had already explained in articles published in the *Transactions of the Society of Arts* and the *Journal of Natural Philosophy*. Later, in a manuscript of reminiscences, Smith acknowledged the help of his amanuensis, Roope, and his friend R.M. Bacon (Editor and Publisher of the *Norwich Mercury*) in putting the work into reasonably good English. The book had been suggested by Coke, to whom it was dedicated, but it was not a financial success. Although two thousand copies were printed, only a few sold at half a guinea (52½p) each. He sold a thousand to a London publisher, John Harding, at less than a fifth of that price and was lucky to do so, as Harding later found himself in financial difficulties.

It was while he was working on draining the coast that he based himself in Norwich (where he usually stayed at the Swan Inn, opposite the tower of St. Peter Mancroft). Here he prepared this treatise on irrigation for publication and his attention was drawn to the processes of the typography used by his friend, Bacon:

> He conceived the idea of continuous printing by causing an inking apparatus to rotate against a revolving frame of type; he drew diagrams and executed models of the requisite surfaces, the type-frame having four plane faces, and the inking frame four faces curved so as to meet them exactly. Mr. Bacon afterwards applied to Mr. B. Donkin to arrange a printing apparatus on this general idea, but under the hands of that eminent engineer it took quite a different form.

Smith did prepare another work to be entitled *Description of Norfolk, its Soil and Substrata* (or possibly *Topographical, Fossilogical and Agricultural Description of Norfolk*). Although its advent was widely advertised in the spring of 1807, only a part of the manuscript had been put into print by August and it was never published. Smith hoped to get some financial assistance from the Board of Agriculture, but this was not forthcoming. He mentions the work in his diary on 23 March 1815, and again in May 1819, but it was not completed or published, and no trace of the manuscript has been found. However, fifty-six printed octavo pages are known to have been bought from the Dawson Turner Collection in 1853 by the London booksellers, T. & W. Boone, who no doubt sold them on. It seems now that they must be presumed lost.

By this time, Smith had almost a monopoly of work for drainage and irrigation, and was constantly engaged in travelling, sometimes covering ten thousand miles in a year, long before the advent of railways and when the quality and quantity of many roads left much to be desired. This had been made a little easier by the inauguration of fast mail coaches on key routes in 1784.

From 1801 to 1809, but particularly from the autumn of 1805 to 1807, he worked steadily to stop seawater flooding the marshlands of Norfolk along a twenty-mile stretch of coast north-west of Yarmouth and to improve the area's drainage. The marshes here were not only below the level of the rivers, that is below the water table, but also liable to flooding from the North Sea (then called the German Ocean) through breaches in the sand hills aggregating to a mile in length. Proposals up to that time had been to build embankments against the sea and use mills to carry away the water from inland areas in particular districts. Smith had difficulty at first in convincing the authorities that it was necessary to exclude the sea from the marshes on a large scale, right across the region. Eventually, in October 1804, the Commissioners of Sewers adopted the plan, and by the end of the summer of 1805 the sea was expelled from seventy-four parishes in Norfolk and sixteen in Suffolk, spread over 40,000 acres (16187 hectares). By The Norfolk and Suffolk Sea Breach Act under James I in 1610, these parishes had been declared liable to contribute to the cost of such works, so they had been considered important at national level for the best part of 200 years.

There was a natural barrier of sand hills, held together by marram (*Arundo arenaria*), with much of the sand being steadily shifted towards the south-east by the action of the sea currents and the wind. Gaps were generated by uneven effects of the wind, allowing the sea to rush in and the land to be spoilt by the salt water, from which it took years to recover. In 1792 there had been nine gaps, totalling 484 yards (443 metres), opposite Horsey. By 1805 new ones had opened, and between Winterton and Happisburgh nearly a mile was open to the sea's advance. Several ideas had been put forward as to how to fill the breach, including the use of stone, clay banks and timber. Smith considered these, but decided that the best method would be to emulate nature, using new embankments set at angles best judged to benefit from the shelter of the old ones. This simple plan required only labour for its execution.

Smith had the embankments made at a relatively shallow gradient of one in twelve, with the back slopes being one in four or five. He noted that at particular seasons and by unusual storms, the sand became uniformly covered by shingle. The pebbles held down the sand against the ravages of the wind. Large numbers of carts were used to remove sand and pile it up across the gaps, sealing it down with a bed of pebbles. Thereafter, maintenance required only minimal expenditure. Smith then turned to draining the land, mostly by using mills to lift the water into rivers.

In September 1802, Smith travelled to North Wales to inspect the successful embankment erected across the Traethbychan at Tremadog. Whilst there, he examined the slate near Dolgellau. He climbed Snowdon to visit a copper mine and studied the slate quarries at Llanberis.

From 1803 he was for several years engaged as a mineral surveyor in Yorkshire, Lancashire, South Wales, Somerset and Gloucestershire. He established a colliery at Torbock, near Liverpool, directed a trial for coal at Spofforth, to the west of York, and looked at the geology of Witton Fell in

Yorkshire. He investigated outcrops of coal near Newent, north-west of Gloucester, in the nearby Forest of Dean, at Nailsea, west of Bristol, and at Kidwelly, south of Carmarthen. He also worked on the construction of sea defences at Laugharne, on the Afon Taf, south-west of Carmarthen.

The quality and details of his observations are typically expressed in his notes dated 6 February, 1803:

> In crossing the Cotswold Hills from Cirencester to Bath, we are above the upper rock to the thirteenth milestone, and in part of this space, from Tetbury to Didmarton, the stuff above it occupies the surface in many places, and produces wheat and pasture land, with plenty of water, slate and wood, which give to the vicinity of Tetbury quite a different appearance to many other parts of the Cotswold Hills. The most perfect part of this upper stratum seems to be about Doughton or I.P. Paul's, and a summit-surface then extends towards Beverstone, which seems to be free from the common intersections even of dry valleys, and continues to Kingscote, and so on in one connected ridge of high ground till it terminates in the bold promontory called Stinchcombe Hill. This point, I believe, is composed of under rock [the upper and under rocks refer to the two oolites of Bath] and its accompanying sand; but I am inclined to think that the upper rock reaches as far as Kingscote, or perhaps to the Gloucester road, which is some distance beyond it. The clay and fuller's earth which lie between the two rocks evidently produce the pasture-land which is about Nimpsfield; and this place is supplied with water from the springs which these strata generally produce. All the streams which flow from this ridge through the many deep vales in different directions must have their source from the same stratum, and I expect that this will be found to be the case with every stream on the western side of the Cotswold Hills from Minchin Hampton to Hawkesbury-Upton, where the two rocks will be found to come very near together in the same hill which constitutes the high ground from thence towards Horton. The outlines of the two rocks then recede from each other again and become much more distinct than I have yet found them on any other part of the Cotswold Hills. The upper rock between the thirteenth and fourteenth milestone dips very considerably towards Badminton Park, and has a very apparent outcrop in the dry freestone land near the thirteenth milestone; the fuller's earth and a bastard blue clay, and the usual accompaniments of those strata, [John Phillips here explains that Smith probably meant the usual fossil shells, especially *Ostrea acuminata*, plentiful in the strata designated], then

> plainly appear by the new plantations going down the hill, and may be traced by the coldness of the surface and outline of the upper rock, which, with two openings through it, runs in a line very near to the Cross Hands and the turnpike road very near Mr. C.'s park. It then returns toward Tormarton (where it appears to have an opening through it), runs out in a ridge at the south side of the park, has an opening through it in the dip, which gives rise to a valley. Cold Ashton, on the opposite side of this vale, plainly points out the line of its corresponding outcrop, which runs round the point of the hill very near the cross ways on the road from Marshfield to Bristol, then returns by the line of the cold wet lands on the south side of the ridge between Cold Ashton and Marshfield. Insulated parts of the upper rock very evidently appear upon the east end of Huntrick's Hill, Charmy Down and Little Salisbury, and to the left run out in another broader part, which includes Toll Down, makes another longer return toward Littleton, and leaves a narrow opening between this line and its opposite outcrop, which stretches from Littleton through Littleton Wood, and, crossing the road by the turnpike, runs out a little way to the right, and returns again to another vale between the parting of the roads and Cold Ashton. The main line before described from Cold Ashton to Marshfield continues in a connected line, which is deeply indented by the many ramifications of the Catherine Stream until it joins the high land at Culeron Down. The crop of this rock may then be traced round by the high part of Mr. Wiltshire's land at Culeron, &c. &c., until it joins the before-mentioned bank on the north side of Cold Ashton, making one connected line all round it, which renders this piece of the upper rock as completely insulated as that on Lansdown or any other of the smaller hills. If we now go back to the thirteenth milestone and look over the face of the country again, it will be readily perceived that the clayey strata of fuller's earth, &c., before described as the source of streams on the western side of the hills, have now become the source of streams which run in a different direction. The sharp rise of the under rock to the west, and the outline of the upper one to the east, before described, form the first outlines of these little hollows, many of which (though dry) may be properly called the primitive source of brooks, rivulets and rivers.

Phillips compared these notes much later with the Ordnance Survey in 1843, and found them remarkably accurate. He comments that:

> the geologist who shall be at the trouble to read this somewhat dry description of observations in the field will require no further evidence to recognise in the author a 'great original discoverer in English geology '.

Around 1803, Smith prepared a map for the new Duke of Bedford. A note entitled *The Principle Strata which are drawn upon the Maps* found among his papers refers to it. It consisted of a list starting with 'Clays and Sand over the Chalk' and continuing:

> The Chalk, the Car Sand and Coral rag, the Blue Clunch and Black laminated Clay, the Oolite Freestone, Blue Lias and Marl, Red Ground and, finally, the Coal Measures.

It is noteworthy that nothing below the Coal is mentioned. This is probably because Smith was very confused about the age of the Carboniferous Limestone, and knew very little about the Old Red Sandstone.

Smith had by now taken rooms in Craven Street, off the Strand in London. A fire broke out there in 1804, and his friend, John Farey, rescued his papers and maps, though they were in some disorder. Smith rented a large house nearby, no.15 Buckingham Street, which Farey had surveyed for him, and he took his geological collections there. For some time, he employed an artist in making drawings for the engraver. He displayed both his maps and his fossils, which with the help of Joseph Townsend, he had set out on sloping shelves to represent the different strata. He was able to show a correlation in age between dissimilar strata which held the same group of fossils. Farey's understanding of Smith's rules were expressed in a simplified form in 1806 as;

> for identifying each particular stratum, either by the knowledge of its relative position with other known strata in its vicinity, by the peculiar organized remains imbedded in it, and not to be found in the adjoining strata, or by the peculiar nature and properties of the matter composing the stratum itself.

The Woburn Sheepshearing in July 1804 is commemorated by G. Garrard, in his painting which hangs in Woburn Abbey. The buildings in the background are those of Park Farm, Woburn. An equestrian Duke of Bedford stands in front of a large column topped by the Ship of Commerce. Many eminent visitors appear in prominent positions, while Smith is shown obscurely in the crowd on the left. Again, Sir Joseph Banks listened to a full explanation of the maps Smith was exhibiting and the ways in which he felt geology should be applied to agricultural practice. Smith had, in fact, prepared a map of the strata specially for Banks's inspection. Sir Joseph was so convinced of its importance that he expressed the view that it must be made public. He took it home to be kept in his library 'for the information of the curious'. He appreciated that Smith would need help towards the cost of publication, and presented him with a cheque for £50 as a generous gesture of support. Although Smith received several other contributions, the plan did not proceed due to the heavy demand for his services. His papers were in London, his fossils in Bath, and he hardly had a moment to look at either. However, Smith remembered Banks's generosity much later, when he dedicated to him his *Map of the Strata of England and Wales*, at last finished in 1815.

On 26 June 1805, he wrote to Richard Crawshay, inviting him, if he were to visit London, to come and see his collection and to have it explained to him. He mentioned in the letter that he had shown his maps to the Duke of Clarence at the Woburn Sheepshearing. These included a large one of the County of Somerset, as a specimen of what could be done right across the country. He also stated that Sir John Sinclair, who had established the Board of Agriculture in 1793, had expressed the view that the Board should have these maps. He had suggested that Smith should be attached to the Corps of Engineers, who were at that time working through the kingdom to create the Ordnance Survey, with a view to connecting his observations to theirs. Smith felt that this would give him a far better opportunity to profit from his important work than he had at the time, as he was experiencing difficulty in marketing it. He stated that his friend, Joseph Townsend, had estimated that it would cost at least £3000 to publish the maps and drawings, which would have to be sold for not less than six guineas (£6.30) per set. The outlay was more than Smith could afford and the price would preclude many potential purchasers. He complained that a number of important people had not come forward with their promised financial support, and he was loath to proceed without it, so that he was minded to publish the work in parts.

It was not until six months later that Richard Crawshay replied, expressing his wholehearted support. He reminded Smith that he had earlier suggested that he should recruit the good offices of an eminent naturalist, Dr. Turton. Nothing came of the suggestion that Smith be attached to the Corps of Engineers, probably because the idea was put forward too early. Thirty years later, a geological branch of the Great Ordnance Survey was established under Sir Henry Thomas De La Beche, FGS, who also founded the Geological Museum and the School of Mines. At every opportunity, Smith acquired records of borings and natural and artificial sections, drew them to a constant scale of twenty-four feet to the inch, and coloured them. He sketched profile sections of most of the roads he traversed, noting natural cliffs and faults. He learned by accident from the owner that a piece of land in south-west Ireland had never been under the plough. He suggested some agricultural improvements, but they fell on deaf ears. However, when he emphasised the importance of investigating any mineral potential, the eventual outcome was the establishment of a very profitable copper mine.

The Geological Society of London was founded in 1807, and a few of Smith's friends were admitted as honorary members, but he himself was overlooked. It seems that his country manner and roughness of speech made him unacceptable in such circles. William Buckland, Reader in Mineralogy at Oxford, remarked that even in 1813 the Geological Society :

> had a very 'landed' manner and only admitted the Professors of Geology in Oxford and Cambridge on sufferance. (J.W. Judd, 1911).

In his *New Light on William Smith and his Work*, L.R. Cox says:

> A few months after the foundation of the [Geological] Society, G.B. [George Bellas] Greenough, the Chairman, accompanied by Sir James Hall and a few other members, condescendingly accepted Smith's invitation to visit his house in Buckingham Street, and there inspected his fossils and maps. They were not in the least impressed by what they saw, and Smith, who had been optimistic as to the results of the visit, soon realised that he could expect no help from this quarter. In fact, not only did no offer of assistance come, but the Society, quite ignoring Smith's efforts, very soon decided to proceed itself with the compilation of a geological map of England, which was to be based, not upon the methods of an ignorant rustic, but upon the principles taught by [Abraham Gottlob] Werner, the great master of the science. At the present day it is a little difficult to imagine the prestige enjoyed by this Saxon teacher, who published very little, but attracted students from all over the world and had the great gift of inspiring them with his doctrines almost as with the spirit of a new religion. His teachings cannot here be expounded in detail, but it may be mentioned that their very gist lay in the doctrine of a series of universal formations which, according to their origin and age, could be classified as Primitive, Transition and Floetz [stratified] rocks. Such terms, and those applied in Saxony to the constituent strata of these main groups, Greenough (as one of Werner's pupils) imagined would prove readily applicable to the rocks of this country.

It is not surprising that the new Society's Chairman, whatever his ideas may originally have been, soon began to meet with difficulties. It seemed most necessary to have the advice of someone with practical experience in geological map-making in this country, and (ignoring Smith) he therefore decided to consult Farey, who at about this time was engaged in his mineralogical survey of Derbyshire. Now, as already seen, Farey had received his original instruction in geology and geological mapping from Smith; he also entertained a hearty contempt for the doctrines of the Wernerian school. The advice which Greenough received from him was, therefore, to abandon the idea of constructing a map on Wernerian principles and to adopt the classification of the strata and the technique which he (Farey) recommended; in other words, to adopt Smith's methods. There is definite evidence from Smith's diaries that he had allowed Farey to examine his geological maps from time to time and even to make copies of them. Farey's maps, which were thus largely based upon Smith's, were shown to Greenough on the understanding that the information obtained from them should be for the private use of members of the Society. Thus it was that a map which was, in broad outlines, based upon Smith's work, began to come into being under the auspices of the Geological Society of London.

3

Rivalry to Smith's Achievement

Smith's expertise continued to be overlooked by The Geological Society. As L. R. Cox continues:

> The sequel is well known. Greenough, with great industry and competence, proceeded with the compilation of his map and was supplied with data for it by several other workers who by now were engaged in active field work in various parts of the country. As the map progressed the desirability of publishing it became obvious, and the original assurance given to Farey that it was for private consultation was soon forgotten. The map was eventually published in 1820, and effectively put a stop to the sale of Smith's, published five years previously, as we shall see. It appeared at a time when Smith, almost overwhelmed with financial and domestic difficulties, was trying to scrape together an existence by surveying certain estates in the south of Yorkshire. A copy which was presented to him reached him at his lodgings at Ferrybridge. 'This copy', he afterwards wrote, 'seemed like the ghost of my old map intruding on my business and retirement, and mocking me in the disappointments of a science with which I could scarcely be in temper. It was put out of sight.'
>
> The above account of the early history of Greenough's map is based, not only on statements subsequently published by Farey [Tilloch, 1820], but upon a MS. note by Smith, part of which it will be of interest to quote. After mentioning that the Society's original intention had been to compile a map on Wernerian principles and that Greenough had consulted Farey on the subject, Smith proceeds, very bitterly, as follows:

> *Knowing what I had done on maps and what he himself had verified by his own observations, he [Farey] disagreed with and quarrelled with the Society for attempting a Wernerian map, and gloried in having beat them off their object; and afterwards threatened to expose their sinister proceedings. That it was better to begin with a map on my principles would be readily admitted by the many members of the Society who had for several years before witnessed what I had done. Farey, it seems, ... they thought best to convert into a friend, and he either lent or gave them a one-sheet map of the stratification of the island - a copy, I think he told me, of the uncoloured MS. one he had before given to me: and, of course, his copy of Cary's large map on which he had so many years before been drawing the lines of strata was also made use of ... And now, as a specimen of the liberality of the leaders of public bodies (for such bodies are generally led by two or three men) I may observe that they proceeded with other of my gratuitously instructed pupils nearly in the same manner as they deal with Mr. Farey, by making them honorary members [Smith appears to have been under a misapprehension, as Farey was not made an honorary member of the Geological Society] and neglecting me - purposely, it would seem, the better to suit their sinister views.*

There is no evidence from Smith's correspondence as to when and how his differences with Farey, arising out of Farey's publication of his results, were composed, as they very quickly seem to have been. After the appearance of his 1806 paper, already mentioned, Farey continued to contribute papers to Tilloch's *Philosophical Magazine* for a number of years, and these include many interesting references to the progress of Smith's work. Perhaps regretting the part he had played in communicating the contents of Smith's maps to Greenough, he became an increasingly aggressive champion of Smith's cause as time progressed, and published in 1815 a paper with the remarkable title *Observations on the Priority of Mr. Smith's Investigations of the Strata of England; on the very unhandsome Conduct of certain Persons in detracting from his Merit therein; and the Endeavours of others to supplant him in the Sale of his Maps*. Unfortunately, Farey rather overdid it. As Fitton [*Edinburgh Review*, 1818] put it, 'the patronage of this gentleman is a little too vehement, and of such a sort, that if he wished to ensure the failure of a valuable performance, we should begin by recommending it to his protection. Smith's reactions to Farey's unsolicited efforts on his behalf are unrecorded. The last paper in which Farey continued to rail at Greenough was published in 1820 and his death occurred in 1826.

However, this is what Greenough himself said about the situation:

> It may be right, however, to mention the geological map of Mr. Smith, because I have been accused of having acted, if not an unfair, at least an ungenerous part, by trespassing upon ground, which I knew to be, by right of preoccupancy, his. I certainly did know, as early as the year 1804, that such a map was begun; but I appeal to all the friends of Mr. Smith, with whom I have conversed on the subject, and especially to the individual who complains of my conduct, whether he, and they did not, for a long time afterwards, in consequence of a variety of circumstances which it is unnecessary to detail, consider its completion, and still more its publication, hopeless. In the belief that the work had been virtually abandoned by Mr. Smith, it was undertaken by me. In 1812, as has already been stated, my map was presented to the Geological Society; and it had been more than a twelvemonth in the hands of the engraver when Mr. Smith published his. I esteem Mr. Smith's map a work of great merit, even when considered abstractedly of the period at which it was undertaken, and the disadvantages under which it was achieved; but I do not think it of a nature to render the publication of mine superfluous. I do not admit that any consideration of justice or delicacy required me either to abstain from constructing my map, in the first instance, or, when partly engraved, to request permission of the Geological Society to withdraw it. Mr. Smith's map was not seen by me till after its publication, and the use I have since made of it has been very limited. The two maps agree in many respects, not because the one has been copied from the other, but because both are correct; and they differ in many, not from an unworthy apprehension on my part of being deemed a plagiarist, but because it is impossible that the views, the opportunities, and the reasonings of two persons engaged on the same subject should be invariably the same.

Greenough was prepared only to accept factual evidence and did not embrace *inferences* suggested not only by Smith but by those even more practically involved such as miners and quarrymen. V.A. and J.M. Eyles (1938) express the view that:

> it would be interesting to know why the Geological Society, of which Greenough was a founder, did not lend its powerful aid to

> Smith to assist him in the publication of his map. Smith, though never a member of the Society, was in contact with members from time to time and numbered some of them among his friends. Whatever the reason, Greenough's map when published was generally acclaimed as vastly superior to that of Smith. Thus, owing to the delay in publication, Smith's map when issued, though not actually still-born, died in infancy, and was succeeded by Greenough's map, which fell heir to much of the glory that should have been Smith's, and attained in 1865 the maturity of a third edition. On this edition only is acknowledgment made to Smith.

A lithographed manuscript in Smith's handwritng came to light early in the twentieth century. It was headed: *Mr. William Smith's Claims to the Discovery and Establishment of Principles which have perfected the System of English Geology.* It reads:

> My Claim to the Original Discovery of 'constancy in the Order of superposition', and 'continuity in the courses of British Strata', with the peculiar mode of identifying them by organized Fossils imbedded, can be supported by many to whom these early observations were communicated: particularly by the Revd. Benjamin Richardson, who in the presence of the late Revd. Joseph Townsend, drew up my first *Tabular Account of British Strata*, printed in my Geological Memoir, Table 1, p. 8. Copies of this Paper were taken by the two Gentlemen present, and another was given to Mr. James, Land Agent.
>
> Reference may also be made to Sir Joseph Banks, The Duke of Bedford, and Mr. Coke, at whose Sheepshearings, and Agricultural and Philosophical Meetings, my original Maps of the Strata were exhibited and explained, from 1799 to 1804; and many original Letters and Papers can be produced.
>
> The Revd. Benjamin Richardson, Revd. Joseph Townsend, Chas. Joseph Harford, Esqr., of Bristol, and The Revd. Richd. Warner were the first of the Scientific Gentlemen in the West who became acquainted with the subject, and immediately adapted my new arrangement of Organized Fossils, in the Order of the Strata which contain them.
>
> In 1799, the information began to spread in Wiltshire, through Mr. Wm. Cunnington, and others, to whom I had explained it, and in the latter part of this year and the beginning of 1800, through Dr. James Anderson, who proposed to insert Papers on the subject in his work called *Recreations on Agriculture.* In 1801,

Proposals were issued for publishing a Quarto Vol. On the subject, and a small Map was lodged with Mr. Debret. In 1802, the late Duke of Bedford had so far satisfied himself of the general accuracy and usefulness of my Discoveries, as to request me, but a few weeks before his Death, to send him specimens of all the Strata and their contents, to be fitted up in their natural Order in a Room at Woburn.

In 1802, The Discovery, and the confirmation thereof by numerous Organized Fossils and other Specimens, was fully explained at Bath, to the late Mr. Wm. Reynolds, of Coalbrook Dale who showed a copy of my original account drawn up in 1799, which, he said, 'was not secret, but to his knowledge had been widely circulated.' Dr. Beddoes, and several other Scientific Gentlemen were of the party.

In the latter part of the same year the subject was explained by Maps & Sections to Mr. Crawshay, who requested me to wait on the Marquis of Bute, to whom the Maps and Papers were fully explained; and again in July 1804, to a large party of Mr. Crawshay's Friends in London.

In May, 1804, this subject was recommended to the attention of the Board of Agriculture by a letter from His Grace the Duke of Bedford, very fully explained at the Woburn and Holkham Sheepshearings; and in July following, His Grace the Duke of Bedford came from Longleat to Bath, to see my Geological Collection, then arranged in the Order of Strata, in small Boxes on the Floor. Dr. Randolph was present at this explanation.

In the autumn of 1804, the Collection was removed to London, and fitted up in the Order of Strata. All this was previous to the establishment of the Geological Society in 1807. Early in 1808, Mr. Greenough and Sir James Hall called in Buckingham Street, and saw the Collection, and on the 8th of March, repeated their visit.

While I was thus spreading the information, and in all parts of the country which I travelled over, practically exhibiting its utility in the various works which I executed, my Brother was spreading it by his works in the West, Mr. Farey in the North, and in all parts by his various Publications, and the Revd. J. Townsend by his works, and, personally, to most of the learned and distinguished visitors of Bath.

Dr. Kidd and others who have since distinguished themselves by Publications on the subject, saw the Original Collection in my house; and by repeated reference to other Collections, similarly arranged ever since my first public disclosure in 1799, any

Gentleman, Foreigners or Natives, had unlimited opportunities of acquiring the most particular knowledge of the subject; and, thus through the great exertions of my truly good friend the Revd. Benjamin Richardson, and the indefatigable Zeal and industry of the Revd. Mr. Buckland, the Science, and probably some of the newly arranged Collection, was transferred from Farley to Oxford.

By this industrious diffusion of the Science, my highly esteemed Friend & others thought they were greatly serving me, and the Country, 'which expects every man to do his Duty,' and that a suitable reward for the Discovery and establishment of English Geology, would not be long withheld.

So rapidly and extensively has the Science spread in the West that Ladies in Wiltshire, and parts adjacent, where specimens of identification are numerous and obtained with facility, have distinguished themselves by these acquirements.

The Geological Society, formed in 1807 of Members whose minds had been purposely, or imperceptibly, stored with this knowledge, could not fail to make the rapid progress for·which they are distinguished. And in the first Vol. of their Transactions, Mr. Parkinson [of Parkinson's Disease fame (described in 1812)], in his Paper on Fossil Remains contained in the Strata near London, observes, that 'this mode of conducting our enquiries was long since recommended by Mr. Wm. Smith, who first noticed that *certain Fossils are peculiar to and are only found lodged in particular Strata, and who first ascertained the constancy in the order of superposition, and the continuity of the Strata of this Island.*

These numerous Public Exhibitions and Explanations of maps, Sections, and Specimens of all the Organized Fossils which identify the Strata; and Presents thereof with their Localities written on them, could not fail to increase and extend the most useful knowledge on the subject; so that Boys of 14 have acquired the Rudiments of the Science, without a word of instruction from me. So industriously and successfully has the Science of British Geology been taught that Hundreds have become practically acquainted with it, without even Books or Hard Names. These are proofs of the simplicity and usefulness of the Science of Geology over any other Science yet established.

The gratification of curiosity, and the satisfactory results of investigation, have alike engaged the young and the old in these pursuits. The acquirement of this useful knowledge in the country is thus rendered very familiar, and every Cabinet of Curiosities becomes tributary to the general stock of knowledge.

This information was, immediately on its development, converted to use by

Mr. Davis in his Valuation;
Mr. Farey in the numerous investigations which his avocations require;
Mr. B. Bevan, in his situation of Engineer;
Mr. Townsend in the compilation of his Book;
Mr. Parkinson, made it an important Article in his 2nd and 3rd vol.,
Mr. Phillips also;
The Encyclopaedia Brittanica [sic](through Mr. Farey) has numerous articles derived from the same source;
The Philosophical and other Magazines;
Philosophical Transactions;

Sowerby's Mineral Conchology, might not otherwise have been published or with much less interest than it now has, and it may be questioned whether The Geological Society would have been so early established without the above-named general diffusion of knowledge on the subject.

The Art of Mapmaking is improved by it; Mr. Cary and Mr. Arrowsmith, in their new Maps having evidently attended to the courses of the Strata in their shading of the Hills.

Thus, while all who could pick up the information thus profusely scattered thought themselves at liberty to publish it, I have been left to pursue, unrewarded and alone, the drudgery of more substantial utility, and my numerous Papers, from want of means, are suffered to remain, from year to year unpublished.

My Claims derived from established Discoveries, which result from 30 years of observation on British Geology, consist:
In having so long back developed the structure of the Earth, in the neighbourhood of Bath, and unravelled the perplexity which the Beds in that neighbourhood exhibit, and made known the Facts & Inferences which they suggested. This enumeration of the West of England Strata was circulated very extensively in MS; and by the exhibitions of Maps also, and Sections of the Stratification in other parts it became a Key to the structure of the remaining part of the Island.

The Elements of the Discoveries thus made public have had a very important though unobserved effect upon the labours of all succeeding enquirers, who have been, perhaps unconsciously, but not the less really, indebted to the Author, for very essential assistance in their progress. Their rapid diffusion of this system amongst the individuals who make up a Nation, and profit by the development of Principles which extend and improve the principal sources of wealth, & greatness in England, does sufficiently establish my Claim to national remuneration.

In thence deducing a particular distinction between the Alluvial and Stratified parts of the Earth's Surface.

In establishing the *order of supposition* of the principal Strata of England & Wales.

In proving their *common declination*.

In identifying the respective Strata by Specimens of Organized Fossils collected from remote parts of each, and depositing them with their Localities in the British Museum as Vouchers thereof.

In drawing Vertical Sections of the Strata, showing how the respective Masses form separate ranges of Hills, and how the great Features of the Island may be thus readily distinguished, by the contours of the Strata and other superficial indications of their courses.

In proving the continuity of these courses of Strata, by accurate delineations of their surfaces and Lines of Escarpment, on Maps of the largest Scale, and publishing the same on a large Map of England & Wales, with other illustrative works.

In having introduced the New Art of Mineral Surveying.

In having discovered and put in practice very extensively a New Art of Draining and improving Land founded on the knowledge of the Strata and of the Springs they produce and also a new mode of supplying Canals with Water, derived from the same Principle; and,

In thence deducing a correct Theory of Springs or an accurate knowledge of the receptacles and Currents of Water in the Earth; which accords with the practice of Mining and Draining, and is thus rendered extremely useful in obtaining water for Canals Brew-houses &c., requiring a large supply; which in some cases may be obtained without Machinery.

As the Public can only judge partially of these labours by the small proportion of my Documents yet before them others who may be engaged in following out & correcting what they suppose to be imperfect, might spare much of that trouble if they knew the extent and accuracy of my yet unpublished Papers.

Wm. SMITH
Civil Engineer
15 Buckingham Street
York Buildings
London

June 1818

In 1809, Smith is found over in Sussex, constructing the Ouse Navigation. Whilst in the area, he visited quarries at Cuckfield, where he found some very large bones, which he added to his collection. Some years later, it was in or near these quarries that Mary Ann Mantell (wife of Doctor Gideon Mantell, eminent geologist as well as physician) came upon an unusually large fossilised tooth. In his *The Riddle of the Dinosaur*, John Noble Wilford suggests that the most likely date of the discovery was August 15, 1820. The tooth was thought at first to have belonged to an iguana, but was later determined to have originated from an unknown prehistoric species, to which Mantell in 1825 gave the name Iguanodon (iguana tooth), the first fully described dinosaur.

Writing in Scarborough in 1839. Smith says:

> I became engineer to the Ouse navigation (the works on which had been abandoned about fourteen years before): and under my management it was extended from the vicinity of Sheffield Place up to the Balcombe Road. Here I found in the names of 'Hammer-ditch,' 'Furnace-pond, Cinder-hills,' &c., the traces of iron-works anciently carried on to a great extent in Sussex: indeed, an elderly gentleman who was one of the commissioners on this business had been one of the Sussex ironmasters. In searching for stone to build the locks and bridges, and by various geological excursions, I became acquainted with the strata, and collected many of the Sussex fossils, some of which were left unnoticed in my Stratigraphical System, from scarcely knowing what strata they belonged to, and which I think is still dubious in much of the interior of the Wealds.
>
> I was, however, sufficiently well acquainted with the stratification to draw its great outlines on the large county map for my friend Mr. Isaac Watt. This, prior to the Ordnance Survey, was considered to be one of the best county maps in England, patronized by, or made at the expense of, the Duke of Richmond.
>
> There being about this time a projected canal through the northern side of the Wealden district surveyed by Mr. Rennie, I took the levels for a line to connect this with the Ouse navigation up the Balcombe Valley, by a tunnel through the forest ridge, and spent some time unprofitably in preparing a plan of it, which was deposited with the Clerk of the Peace at Lewes.

The project to which Smith refers here was probably that for the Grand Southern Canal, which was to connect the Medway to Portsmouth. It was to start at Tonbridge and run for ninety-five miles through Edenbridge, Crawley, Horsham and Pulborough, to join the River Arun 1¼ miles above Arundel Bridge.

In 1810 the authorities in Bath were alarmed to find a threat to the prosperity of the city, caused by the failure of its hot springs which supplied the Baths and the

Pump Room. Smith was asked to investigate the situation and, against opposition, opened up the hot-bath spring to its bottom. He discovered that the springwaters had not in fact failed, but were flowing away along a new channel. Conditions in the pit were oppressive, the temperature reaching 119° F (48° C), causing the tallow candles to melt. He stopped up the outflow, thus restoring, and in fact improving, the supply of hot mineral waters to the spa. The discharge of hot water was said to be over 260 gallons (1182 litres) per minute. At Batheaston, three miles to the north-east of the city, there was serious flooding of a newly-sunk coal-pit, which was imagined by some to have been the cause of the altered flow of the springs. The hot water at Bath was coming up from a great depth through a subterranean fault, and was hardly likely to have affected a coal-pit three miles away and some forty to sixty feet higher. In any case, Smith was successful in checking the Batheaston flooding.

John Phillips writes:

> He exhibited on many occasions a considerable facility in mechanical inventions. When the bore-hole in the pit sunk at Batheaston had reached the lias so much water sprung up as to fill the pit, and overpower the engine. What was to be done? Smith instantly met the case by a very simple arrangement. He caused a long piece of wood to be planed with eight sides tapering to a point; at the large end he screwed on a heavy iron top, and to an eye in this was fastened a rope of sufficient length and strength. The machine (if it may be so called) was let down to the pit bottom, and moved about in the water till the point of the rod entered the bore-hole; it was then permitted to drop into it: the iron head was unscrewed, lifted, and again permitted to fall as a hammer on the rod, which by three or four blows became fixed in the hole. Thus the spring was stopped, so that the engine, being set to work again, easily emptied the pit.'

During the period 1804 to 1813, Smith produced a number of sections, including one at Batheaston, in an often unsuccessful but wholly scientific attempt to find coal. He was one of the first to demonstrate how much could be gained from the record of such negative evidence. It is noteworthy that such sections were only rarely made, and hardly ever kept. At this time, there were many mines sunk in trials for coal, some without any geological reason and thus large amounts of money were invested to achieve nothing. In some cases, Smith warned the speculators against proceeding, often to no avail. He reported on trials for coal in Buckinghamshire and was soon back in South Wales to plan and survey improvements in Kidwelly Harbour, to the south of Carmarthen.

The next year, he was called in to track down the causes of leakage in the Kennet and Avon Canal. It ran through an area where subterranean streams were responsible for landslips, blowholes and breaches in canals. It was the regular alternation of oolitic limestone, with its open-jointed rocks, and the impervious clays, which was the cause of numerous springs. These were very difficult to deal with. Also, where the line of the canal ran across wide stretches of limestone, even great expense and all the skills of the engineer were sometimes not enough to prevent the water flowing away as fast as it was supplied. Small faults and landslides would divert some of the springs, allowing them to erode the puddling in the bottom or sides of the canals. There was also the problem of deep-rooting plants and small burrowing animals penetrating the banks. Smith supervised extensive excavation to intercept all the springs and either collect the water in natural reservoirs, from which it could be ducted to supply the canal, or divert it safely beneath the cut.

Writing from 15 Buckingham Street in 1811, Smith reported, in conjunction with a Mr. Martin, on *The Strata of the Collieries at and near Nailsea*, in connection with the Bristol and Taunton Canal. He expressed the view that the colliery had enough extractable coal to justify the construction of a canal.

Smith was next (in 1811-12) called back to the Somersetshire Coal Canal, where serious leakages were occurring. He also went over to Suffolk to undertake drainage work at Minsmere. All this travelling gave him wonderful opportunities to see at first hand the geology of the country, and he made daily notes of his experiences. However, it is no wonder that he had no time to prepare his maps and books for publication.

On Christmas Day 1800, William Smith's sister had borne a son, John Phillips. The lad was orphaned at the age of seven and became his uncle's ward. He was given a good classical education in Wiltshire, then spent a year with the Rev. Benjamin Richardson, an Oxford graduate and gifted naturalist. At the age of fourteen he came to live with Smith and spent many years as his assistant, and later his partner, frequently accompanying him on his professional engagements, at his lectures and on field trips. He learned so much from his uncle that, at the age of thirty-three, he was appointed Professor of Geology at King's College, London, was elected F.R.S. in 1834, and ten years later became Professor of Geology and Mineralogy at the University of Dublin. In the 1840s he proposed the division of the geological time-scale into eras - Palaeozoic, Mesozoic and Cenozoic. In 1844, he published *Memoirs of William Smith, LL.D.,* the only detailed biography of his uncle. Subsequently he took up the Chair of Geology at Oxford, was elected President of the Geological Society of London (1851-60), and was Keeper of the Ashmolean Museum (1854-1870). He died in 1870.

4

The Culmination and Reception of Smith's Work

Smith had used the maps produced by John Cary, a London engraver and publisher, for his early illustrations of local geology. In 1812, Cary generously offered to publish his geological map of England and Wales (on which he had been working for twenty years). The plates were specially made to Smith's specification, omitting political boundaries and other irrelevancies but including in detail small streams, which Smith considered an important feature of physical geography. In a note dated September 3 1813, he wrote:

> It being my wish to render the map as interesting as possible to those who are desirous of knowing all they can of their country, none but the most descriptive names have been introduced except where these were not sufficiently numerous and it was necessary to introduce places well known on the public roads. In consequence of this selection of names which only appertain to the subject of soil and substrata, the names of many places of considerable consequence have been omitted and others introduced which a general observer may think too insignificant....

Smith even thought at this time of producing an *Index Villaris*, to go with his map, featuring his ideas of the derivation of numerous place names, but he never brought the idea to fruition. He showed his understanding of the value of plants in geological mapping in a letter to his friend, the Rev. Benjamin Richardson, dated 11 February, 1813, in which he said:

> As the season for a revival of the locality of indigenous plants is just approaching, I hope you will not forget to make a complete list of them on each stratum. This, with your able assistance, would form a most interesting chapter, and would serve to draw

> the attention of many to the subject of strata, who probably might otherwise never think of it.

In December 1813, Smith spent twelve days in Yorkshire, based at Larpool Hall, near Whitby. This was the home of Edmund Peters, who had asked him to survey a new approach road to the house and to prepare and copy maps of his estate. The main purpose of his visit was, however, to report on two coal-mining ventures at Gnipe How, in the shore cliffs south-east of Whitby, and at Borrowby, on the moors nine miles to the north-west. The thin seams of low-grade Jurassic coal had been mined in the area since 1648, but, as Smith reported, they were difficult and expensive to work. They were only an economic proposition at all, because supplies from elsewhere could not be obtained cheaply, and the coal was needed for burning lime to provide fertiliser. At Gnipe How the adit was only accessible at low tide, and the operation was restricted to the summer months, because the coal had to be carried on the backs of donkeys up a dangerous path 250 feet (76m) to the clifftop. At Borrowby, the seams were no more than eighteen inches thick, making them extremely difficult to work, with much waste material to be dispersed. It was the sparsity of wood and the lack of a good harbour to bring coal in from further afield that made mining for it here a necessity, if the poor quality land was to be made agriculturally productive. Smith suggested that the tenants of the land should be the ones to work the coal and that they should begin where it outcropped, working upwards, so that any water would drain away without the necessity for pumps. Some of the information he obtained on this visit featured on his geological map of Yorkshire published seven years later.

He spent the next two years adding the geological details, using his novel feature of shading each formation darker at its base. This clarified the boundaries of each stratum. With the help of Henry Jermyn of Sibton Abbey in Suffolk, a barrister he had met and become friendly with while draining Minsmere Marshes near Dunwich, he devised a number of new descriptive names of places from Greek and Latin.

He had achieved success at Minsmere by channelling the water from the marsh into a large-bore cast-iron pipe. This was buried deep in the shingle and was not quite covered at high tide by the sea, but it prevented the salt water from passing through itself by three sets of closing doors set one above the other. As the tide fell, the doors opened in sequence under the water pressure from the landward side and the fresh water slowly drained into the sea.

In 1814, Smith carried out survey work in the coalfields of Cheshire, inspected sea defences near King's Lynn in Norfolk, and spent time in Suffolk, Kent and the Forest of Dean. Such spare moments as he had were occupied in completing his *Map of the Strata*. He was able to explain some of the sheets to Lord Hardwicke, the President, and other members of the Board of

Agriculture. Following this, one of them, Benjamin Hall, M.P. for Glamorganshire and son-in-law of Richard Crawshay who had recently died, asked for a second and private presentation. He reminded Smith of his father-in-law's great interest in his work, and that he had only paid half of the £100 he had promised him before his death. Hall proposed to give Smith the other half and to add to it his own subscription. Later, several eminent men, including Sir Joseph Banks, Coke, the Duke of Bedford and Lord Hardwicke, came forward with funds at a time when Smith was in dire need of them. Smith's innovative method of colouring, with stronger tints defining the edges of the strata, needed careful checking and proved unexpectedly costly. John Cary paid liberally for the labour involved.

On 7 June 1814, Smith demonstrated his map to the Board of Agriculture. Shortly afterwards, he sent to its members a printed circular, which read:

> The BOARD OF AGRICULTURE having sanctioned Wm. Smith's Map of the Strata of England and Wales as a Work highly deserving of Encouragement, and recommended him to send Copies of his Prospectus to every Member; he takes the earliest opportunity of acknowledging his great Obligations to that Honourable Board, and particularly to the Right Honourable President the Earl of Hardwicke, and several other Members, who have expressed their most earnest Desire to have the Whole of William Smith's Mineralogical Survey published without delay.
>
> The Members of the Board of Agriculture are therefore most respectfully informed, that William Smith will explain the Subject of Strata, at his House, 15, Buckingham Street, Strand, on this and following Days, between the Hours of Eleven and Five, to such Gentlemen as choose to subscribe toward the Publication of this great national Work. W. Smith's Discoveries of Regularity in the Strata, with their accompanying organic Remains, will be illustrated by Engravings of his large Collection of Fossils, which are placed in the same Order as they lay in the Earth.

A letter to Smith from his friend, Richardson, suggests that the Prime Minister (the Earl of Liverpool) was among those who called on him to listen to his presentation.

In May 1815, the map was at last completed. On 23 May, Smith attended a meeting of the Board of Agriculture with the first finished copy on canvas. It was a remarkable achievement for the work of one man, and the amount of information it contained was enormous. It is one of the classics of English science. Between 1794 and 1813, the Board of Agriculture had issued reports containing geological information and maps in respect of fourteen counties, but this was the first published large-scale geological map of England and

Wales. It formed the basis for all subsequent maps of its type. It was on a scale of five miles to the inch and comprised fifteen sheets measuring in total six foot by eight foot six inches (1.8 by 2.6m) There was also a small-scale topographical index chart. It took up to eight days for an artist to colour the first printed copy, and twenty different tints were used. It was entitled:

> *A / DELINEATION / of the / STRATA / of / ENGLAND and WALES, / with part of / SCOTLAND; / exhibiting / the COLLIERIES and MINES, / the MARSHES and FEN LANDS ORIGINALLY OVERFLOWED BY THE SEA, / and the / VARIETIES of SOIL / according to the variations in the substrata, / ILLUSTRATED by the MOST DESCRIPTIVE NAMES / By W. SMITH.* To the Right Honble. Sir Joseph Banks Bart., P.R.S. / This Map is by Permission most respectfully dedicated / by his much obliged Servant, / W. SMITH, Augst. 1, 1815.

Beneath the lower margin is printed, 'Published by J. CARY, 181, Strand, London: August 1st, 1815.' It was exhibited in London to the Board of Agriculture, to the Royal Institution and to the Society for the Encouragement of Arts, Manufactures and Commerce. This society had offered annually, since 1802, a premium of fifty guineas for a mineralogical map of England and Wales. Smith had submitted a completed copy to them on 8 February 1815, and received this award which he might well have claimed much earlier, but for the deep-seated desire to complete the work to his own satisfaction. From then on, Smith's fame as a great original discoverer in English geology was assured.

On the map, the mountain ranges are shown, including the peaks of Snowdon, Scafell and Skiddaw, coloured in and indicated as 'Killas and Slate' with patches of 'Granite'. Major spot heights are given in feet. The Wye Valley contains 'Red and Dunstone' and 'Limestone', with 'Coalmeasures' marked to the south-east. Another bed of 'Limestone' separates this from the 'Red Marl', 'Lias' and 'Blue Marl' of the Vale of Severn. The 'Under Oolite' comes next, tinted in red, followed by the 'Freestone'. The 'Vale of Isis' has 'Forest Marble', 'Cornbrash', 'Clay', 'Sand' 'Limestone' and 'Sand' again, followed by 'Chalk', and in the Thames Valley there is 'Brickearth' and 'London Clay'. The strata all dip to the south-east, and the formation of valleys and escarpments is clearly shown. Conventional signs are used to mark canals, tunnels, tramways and roads, collieries, lead, copper and tin mines, together with salt and alum works.

In the *Geology Magazine* 1897, Professor J.W. Judd summarised the main defects of the map:

> The representation of the Tertiaries was very inadequate, no indication of the Crags being given, the Isle of Wight Tertiaries, the Bagshot Beds of Southern England, and the Boulder-clays of

> East Anglia being all confounded together, and the relation of these to the London Clay being left obscure. The Wealden Area was altogether unsatisfactorily treated, the argillaceous strata being coloured as 'Oaktree Clay' and the arenaceous as ironsand (Lower Greensand, etc.). Lastly, the Jurassic estuarine strata of North Yorkshire were confounded with the 'carstone and ironstone' of the South-East of England. On the other hand, it is interesting to note that Smith had already learned at this early date the existence of strata lying between the Old Red sandstone and the slaty rocks of Wales and Cumberland. These have a tablet assigned to them in his legend with the description 'various alternations of hardstone, limestone and slate', though the information he possessed was not sufficient to enable him to extend proper colours for them to the map. This is probably the earliest notice of the strata afterwards made so famous by the researches of Murchison and his coadjutors.

This criticism was made, after all, eighty-two years after the publication of Smith's map, and in the light of a great deal more knowledge acquired since.

The map was offered in six different forms:

Price, in Sheets, with the Memoir	£ 5 5 0
Mounted on Canvass and Rollers	£ 7 0 0
Ditto, ditto, and varnished	£ 8 0 0
Ditto, fitted in a Case for Travelling	£ 7 0 0
Ditto, on Spring Rollers	£ 10 0 0
Ditto, ditto, varnished	£ 12 0 0

By March 1816, 250 copies had been painted in watercolours and issued to subscribers; most of the maps were numbered and signed by Smith and duly noted in his diary. V.A. and J.M. Eyles (1938) recorded their findings after a careful examination of twenty-seven copies. They were able to show that between 1815 and 1819, Smith constantly made alterations to his map, as further prints were coloured. Sometimes this was done before the printing plates had been altered, so that the colour wash disagreed with the printed boundaries. Smith would have known that many copies were out of date when they were published. With his conscientious temperament, he would have been most unhappy about it, but Cary refused to bear the loss if numerous copies already printed were discarded. The map retailed at five guineas (£5.25) a copy but the costs of production and colouring may well have absorbed most of the proceeds. It was a great cartographic and scientific achievement, representing as it did some 65,000 square miles (166,400 sq. km) and being the first large-scale geological map of any country. Its accuracy is amazing and it stands comparison with modern geological maps and stratigraphic columns. Smith had originally hoped to have 750 printed. Early subscriptions were for 414 copies, but some potential purchases were not taken up. It seems unlikely that many more than that were sold. Fewer than a hundred are known to be extant.

Probably none was sold after 1820. The likely reasons for this were threefold. As we have seen, within five years Greenough had published a better map under the auspices of the Geological Society. From 1 January 1819, Smith issued geological maps of individual English counties, and the information on these was more correct than on his large publication. In March 1820, Cary issued a small-scale (fifteen miles to the inch) geological map of England and Wales by William Smith. Several significant changes had been made to the information that had featured on Smith's large map, including the geological colouring of parts of Ireland and France, the addition of some granite masses in south-west Scotland and a number of dykes and sills (known then as 'trap') in the Clyde/Forth Valley and Wales.

In 1815, soon after his great map was published, Smith produced a book entitled *A Memoir to the Map and Delineation of the Strata of England and Wales, with part of Scotland.* This, too, is dedicated to Sir Joseph Banks, and contains a list of about 400 subscribers to the work. It consisted of fifty-one pages and two folding tables, and is divided into four sections:

> Introduction; Explanation of the Subject of Strata, and of the Colours by which they are represented on the Map; General Account of the Soil and Substrata in the Respective Counties; and Characteristic Distinctions of Soil and Surface in the Courses of the respective Strata, described in the Order in which their edges successively terminate.

In the *Memoir*, he expressed in his own words, probably for the first time, the great discovery he had made with regard to the different strata having their own typical fossils, wherever they are found, the maxim which is the foundation of the science of geology:

> The immense sums of money imprudently expended in searching for coal and other minerals, out of the regular course of the strata which constantly attend such productions; and in forming canals, where no bulky materials were afterwards found to be carried upon them; prove the necessity of better general information on this extensive subject. And I presume to think, that the accurate surveys and examinations of the strata, as well near the surface of the earth as in its interior, to the greatest depths to which art has hitherto penetrated, by the sinking of wells, mines, and other excavations, to which I have devoted the whole period of my life,

> have enabled me to prove that there is a great degree of regularity in the position and thickness of all these strata; and although considerable dislocations are found in collieries and mines, and some vacancies in the superficial courses of them, yet that the general order is preserved; and that each stratum is also possessed of properties peculiar to itself, has the same exterior characters and chemical qualities, and the same extraneous or organised fossils throughout its course. I have, with immense labour and expense, collected specimens of each stratum, and of the peculiar extraneous fossils, organic remains, and vegetable impressions, and compared them with others from very distant parts of the island, with reference to the exact habitation of each, and have arranged them in the same order as they lay in the earth; which arrangement must readily convince every scientific or discerning person, that the earth is formed as well as governed, like the other works of its great Creator, according to regular and immutable laws, which are discoverable by human industry and observation, and which form a legitimate and most important object of science. The discoveries and improvements, both in mining and in agriculture, which are now confined to a few parts of the kingdom, may be fully extended to many more, and in some degree to all, by a better knowledge of geology; and a faithful general view of the soil and substrata of our island (in which no beds are omitted that can well be described in such a map) will be found a work of great convenience, in considering the various applications which are made to the legislature for canals, roads, and railways alone.

The volume includes a table entitled *Order of the STRATA and their imbedded ORGANIC REMAINS, in the Vicinity of Bath; examined and proved prior to 1799*. It is remarkably complete and comprises twenty-three different beds from the Chalk to the Coal.

The plates for Smith's large map survived until 1877. On 12 July of that year, Professor G.S. Boulger, a Member of the Scientific Club, published a letter in the *Geological Magazine*. It read:

> Sir, At a recent sale the copper-plates of William Smith's original folio atlas of geologically coloured maps of England, sixteen in number, including the index, published in 1821 [sic], came into the possession of Mr. Edward Stanford of Charing Cross, who is willing to sell them at, as he writes to me, a trifling cost (for sixteen large coppers), if purchased for the Geological Society. It would not pay now-a-days to reprint maps only of historical

21. Tramway route on the east side of Tucking Mill House.

> interest; but I venture to think that the maps of the father of English Geology are worthy of being preserved from the melting-pot, the doom of superannuated copper plates, and entrusted to the safe keeping of some chartered society. I write this, therefore, to obtain the opinion of geologists on the matter, and shall be glad to receive the names of gentlemen who will subscribe to their purchase, as I propose, for presentation to the Geological Society, which already possesses the original manuscript maps.

There was no response to this appeal and the plates were melted down.

With the end of the Napoleonic wars in 1815, the exchange of scientific information was facilitated. The world's finest zoological and palaeontological museum had been built up in the state-supported Jardin du Roi in Paris. Georges Cuvier, Professor of Natural History at the Collège de France, Paris, (who became known as the father of comparative anatomy and palaeontology), collaborated with Members of the Geological Society in the exchange of data and specimens. There was, over the next ten years, a growing realisation of the importance of fossils and their relation to strata. Philosophical societies were founded in Bristol, Cambridge, Dublin, Manchester and particularly in Yorkshire, where a profusion of fossils was there for the taking, especially at Whitby and other locations along the coast. Interest here was stimulated by the publication in 1817 of George Young's *History of Whitby,* which directed public opinion towards the importance and significance of fossil remains. Collecting became fashionable, and there were established dealers in Bridlington and elsewhere. As the County Town, York took the lead, but significant displays were amassed for museums in Hull, Scarborough and Whitby.

Smith's ideas and contribution to the new science began slowly to be appreciated. However, a proposal in 1822 by Dr. William Henry Fitton (later himself to accept the Chair of the Geological Society) that Smith be elected an Honorary Member was vetoed by Greenough, the incumbent President, presumably on the grounds of Smith's impecunious background.

In 1811, he had acquired Kingham Quarry, off Summer Lane on Combe Down, half a mile north of Tucking Mill. He had bought it from his neighbour, Charles Conolly, owner of Midford Castle, a folly to the north-west of the mill. He constructed a tramway to bring the freestone down to a wharf on the Coal Canal. It is thought that Smith also obtained sand (Midford Sand) here for use in bread oven floors. Smith also set up in partnership with Conolly, who owned the land over which the top part of the tramway ran, and installed cutting and shaping machinery to dress the stone. Unfortunately, the stone turned out to be of poor quality, which Smith of all people should have realised. It failed to find a market, leaving Smith deeply in debt.

In desperation, he offered to sell his highly-prized fossil collection to the Government. A page from his diary indicates that he was paid a personal visit

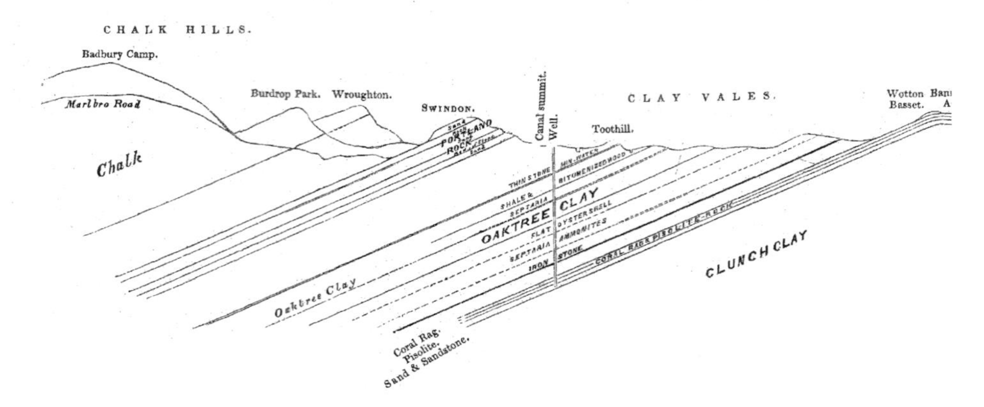

22. A section of the strata, North Wiltshire, as drawn by Smith.

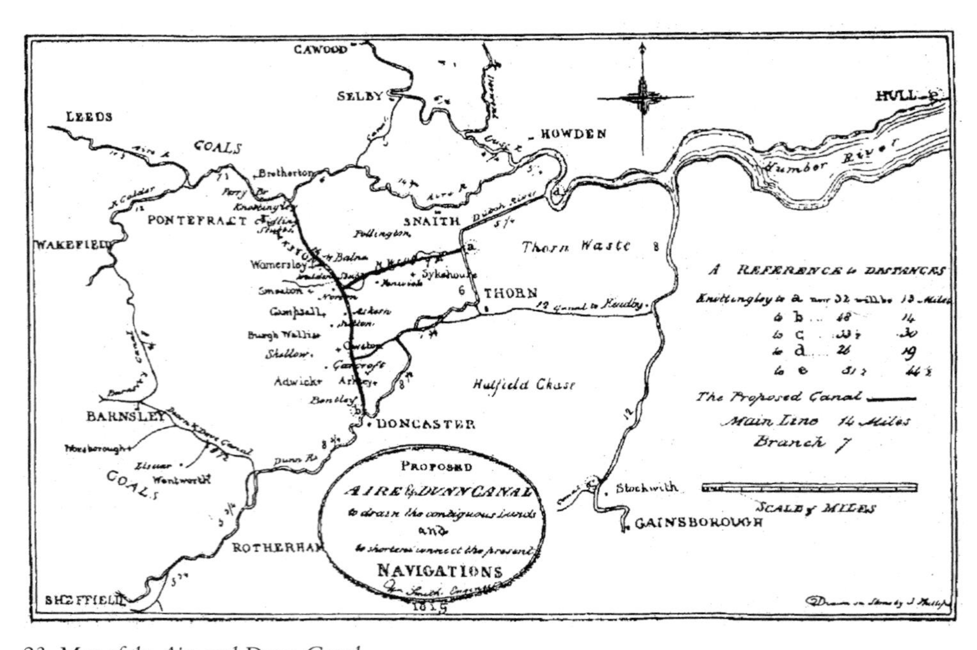

23. Map of the Aire and Dunn Canal.

on 1 July 1815 by the Chancellor of the Exchequer, Nicholas Vansittart, who came with James Brogden, M.P., Chairman of the Ways and Means Committee and Sir John Stanley. Smith drew up a memorandum to the Treasury, extolling the value of his collection to the nation. He had received no reaction by late September and wrote urgently to Thomas Hoblyn, Senior Clerk in the Treasury, requesting an advance of £500 to £700, to avoid his having to sell his interest in his great geological map. The Treasury minutes record that in early October, the Lords Commissioners charged Charles Hatchett, a chemist and mineralogist, and Joseph Planta, Principal Librarian and head of the British Museum staff, with assessing the value of the collection. They visited Smith's house, accompanied by Charles Konig, Curator of the Natural History Collections in the British Museum, on 10 October. Their report published a week later criticised the fact that the collection was not well catalogued. Smith had such a good memory that he had up to then had no need of a catalogue, but he undertook to produce one without delay. The Treasury agreed to advance him £100 immediately.

A month later, John Phillips (then fourteen years of age) joined his uncle to help him with arranging the collection. By 3 December, Smith had completed a *Table of the Genera of Organic Remains in the Different Strata.* With the help of a good friend, William Lowndes, Chief Commissioner of the Tax Office and an amateur geologist who had the ear of the Chancellor, Smith obtained the promise of a further £400 in instalments as and when the fossils were deposited safely in the British Museum. However, there was a problem - the museum was not ready to receive the collection, and it was not until 18 June 1816 that it was at last delivered. Smith received his final settlement two days later. There was a suggestion that Smith should supervise the presentation of his fossils in the museum and explain the geological principles which they portrayed, but this did not materialise. In February 1818, he was granted another £100 for a further series of fossils collected from Essex, North Wiltshire and other localities, and an additional £100 for arranging and cataloguing his collection, which was thought to contain 2657 specimens of 693 species, collected at 263 different localities. They were arranged on sloping shelves to represent the strata in which they were found. Smith saw the stratification as the product of successive creations, though the amount of time involved was not clear. He understood that there was a chronological significance in his fossil discoveries, and he took note not only of characteristic fossils but of the whole picture of the contents of individual strata, be the fossils plentiful or not.

There were then no departments of palaeontology or geology in the British Museum, and there were difficulties in fitting the collection compatibly into the other public exhibits. It seems that it was relegated to drawers and little attention paid to it until 1885-6, when the displays in the new galleries at South Kensington were being arranged under the direction of Dr. Henry

Woodward. The value and significance of the collection was then recognised, though about a quarter of the specimens have now disappeared, possibly disposed of as 'duplicates'. The care with which Smith labelled each item is very clear. The larger fossils had written on them in Indian ink the localities where they were found, and the smaller ones carry a reference mark, usually consisting of a combination of a Roman capital, a number and a small letter. Smith gives the meaning of this in the introduction to his *Stratigraphical System of Organised Fossils*, published in 1817, which consists of a detailed catalogue of the specimens deposited in the Museum:

> On the specimens, Roman capitals mark the genus, - the figures, 1,2,3, &c., refer to the species, - and the small letters, a,b,c, &c., to the localities or sites in the Strata.

Most of the specimens were carefully relabelled by Mr. Robert Etheridge.

5

Financial Crisis

In 1816, the Wilts and Berks Canal Company was faced with the problem of supplying sufficient water to its own summit level and to supply the locks lower down on the North Wilts Canal. They tried sinking an artesian well without geological advice in the valley between Swindon and Wootton Bassett, and had bored initially some 240 feet (73m) down without success, before they called in William Smith. His report, datelined Swindon 13 April 1816, is a good example of the way in which he went about his business:

> In order to form a correct opinion of the success of the experiment for water now going on by the side of the Wilts and Berks Canal, I have particularly examined the nature of the earth sunk and bored through, and endeavoured by local observations to ascertain the extent of the stratum now penetrating, and the nature of the rock beneath, which is expected to produce the supply of water required.
>
> The stratum in which the pit has been sunk to the depth of 46 yards, and bored into near 50 yards deeper, is chiefly a tenacious clay, containing at certain depths layers of the *Septarium* or *Ludus Helmontii*, very similar to those from which Parker's Roman cement is made.
>
> These stony nodules the sinkers have called rock, but no regular rock has yet been found, nor is there any hope of finding any until the whole stratum of clay is penetrated. The depth of such a perforation can only be judged of by similar experiments for coal and water in various places along the course of this extensive stratum. Here the depth was, of course, expected to be great, from the known depth of several deep wells in the neighbourhood, all of which produced water which ascended to their tops; and the deepest and nearest to this experiment having done so and continued to overflow ever since it was sunk,

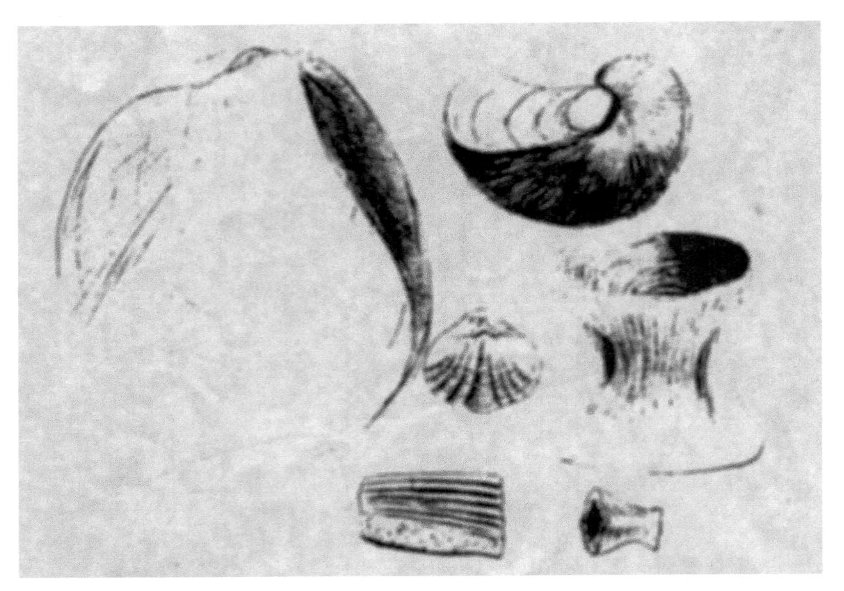

24. Rough draft of an unpublished plate (lias fossils) intended for Smith's Strata Identified by Organized Fossils.

afforded data for such a proceeding. Besides the water found at Mr. King's of Mannington Farm, I find that water has been obtained at another farm of his and at Costar and Whitefield, along the course of the same clay-ridge which extends to Wotton Basset; and that at three of these wells, like that of Mr. Edwards's well (at Even Swindon), the water is of a mineral quality. All of them, I am informed, have a copious supply of water, and stand full to the surface; or nearly so, which proves the original source or head of the water to be on high ground. This my extensive and long-continued observations on the strata led me to expect; and the order of the strata is that which I have always thought it to be, a thick stratum of clay overlying the coral rag and upper oolite rocks, which crop out or appear on the surface at Wotton Basset.

To apply this general knowledge of the strata to the situation in question, I have particularly examined the outcrops and extent of surface occupied by that stratum of limestone, as much of the success of the present experiment must depend upon the extent and cavities for water in the stratum which underlies the clay.

The surface of this rock about Wotton Basset is very narrow and interlayered with clay, but between Lidyard and Purton much more extensive and absorbent, terminating about the latter place on the borders of the River Roy, in long narrow ridges sloping to the east, with a partial declination toward the south or

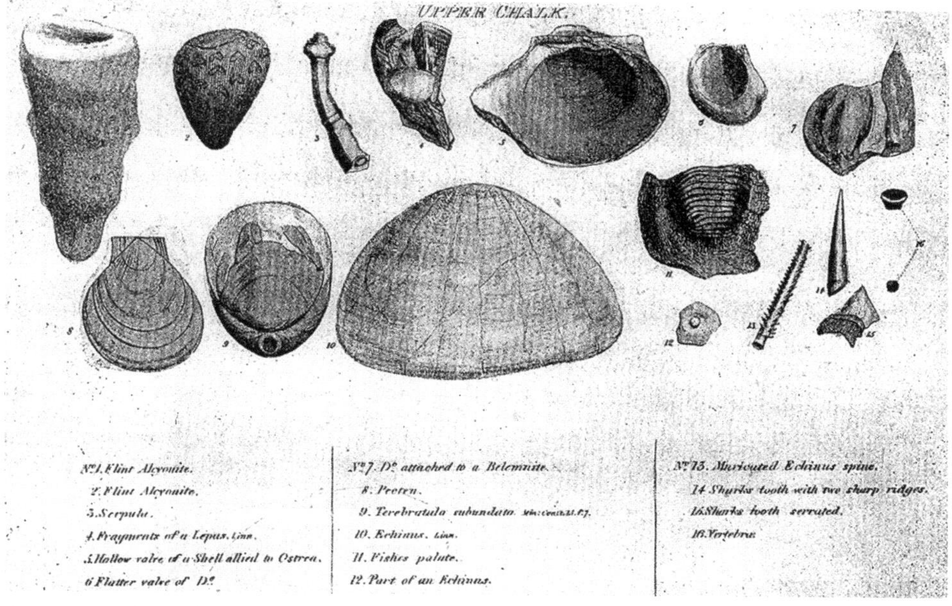

25. Upper chalk fossils.

south-west, which has a tendency (with the other outliers of the rock) to form a basin or trough, whose deepest part is near the present boring hole, and consequently the greatest quantity of water which the rock will produce may be there expected. Thus far is the theory of finding water at that situation correct, but there may be some practical objections to the quantity it will produce:-

1st. The top part of the rock is covered, and frequently interlayered with clay.
2nd. The whole rock is not above 20 or 30 feet thick.
3rd. It has but few open joints, and those not very large.

Consequently the faults in the declination of these strata to the east or south-east may frequently interrupt the general descent of water to one point in the deep, and occasional considerable partial discharges of the water absorbed, as I found in the little valley below Purton.

Yet this copious discharge from one or two hundred acres of land serves rather to prove how much the remainder of the rock, which has no visible discharge, may be expected to produce. Water will most probably soon be found, which may be expected to rise to the surface, but with such a head upon it, the discharge

Geological System

Introduction

Connection of British Strata with those of adjacent Countries

— Exterior form of the Island —

Terminations of Strata in the Sea

Bays,	High Cliffs,
Estuaries of Rivers,	Low Shores,
Capes,	Mutability of the Coast.

— Interior of the Island. —

General Observations and Classes of Strata

— Principles of natural Drainage —

Introductory Remarks.	Peculiar appearances of
Summits of Drainage.	the Streams of each Stratum
Theory of Springs and of the	Lakes.
courses of streams,	
Illustrated by reference to	Low Marshy Grounds of
particular streams.	the Interior

— Variations from the general regularity of the Strata —

Subterraneous Elevations, and	Unconformableness of the courses
Depressions influencing the	of outcrop of several Strata,
undulations on the Surface of the Earth,	Faults, or apparent Dislocations of Strata.

— Locality of Plants, and of free Animals, —

as influenced by the Properties of the Strata.

— Sites of Population, —

Origin of Towns, Villages, and Seats and Parks of Nobility and Gentry.
— as influenced by advantages arising from the Properties of the Strata —

27. Draft of the title page of the Geological System, a work projected by Smith in 1817.

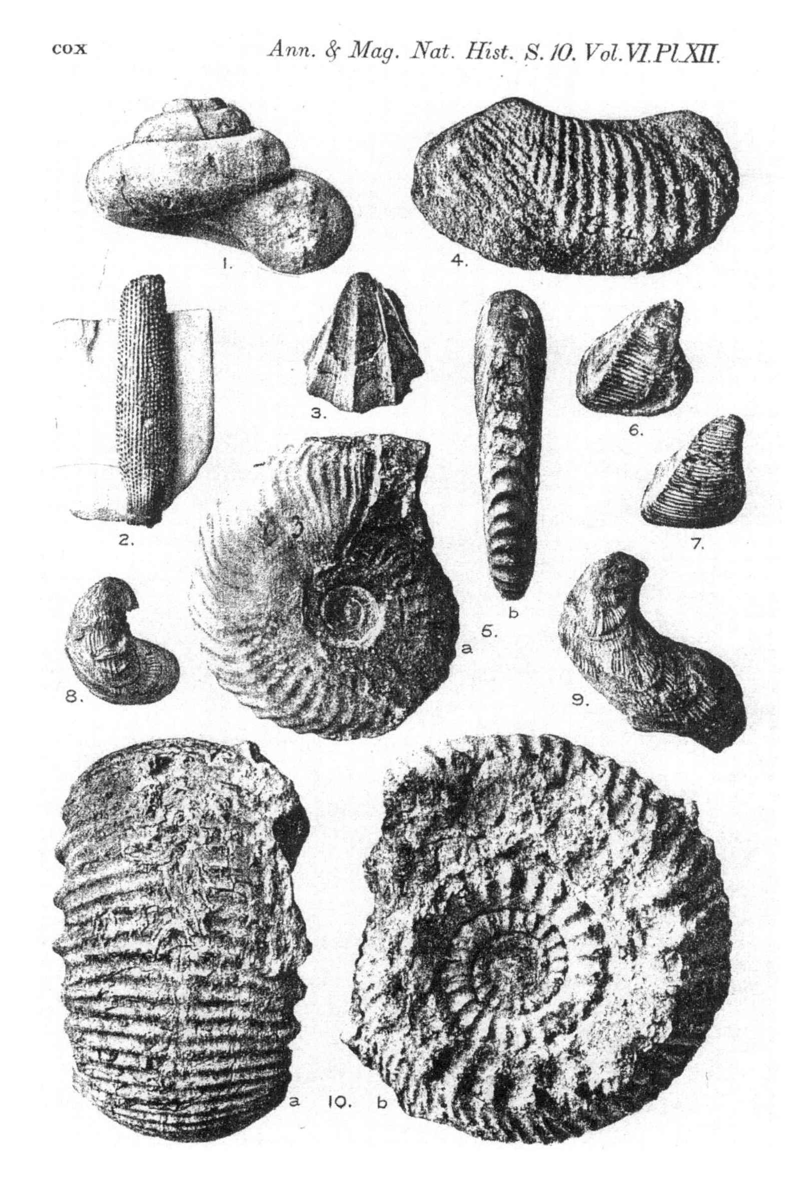

26. Fossil species named by William Smith.

> will be slow unless it be assisted by machinery, and the natural apertures at the bottom of the pit enlarged by some tunnelling into the rock; all of which is very practicable. Should there be any variation in the quantity of water, it is generally, under such circumstances, most abundant in summer.

Needless to say, Smith's predictions proved correct. The boring continued and when the coral rag and oolite were reached, a small amount of water was encountered. As the well was deepened the water increased, until the bore reached 260 feet (79m), the lowest fifteen of which were through solid rock. There was now a considerable volume of water, which brought up with it large quantities of sand from below the limestone, filling between fifteen and eighteen feet of the well. The engineers had to call in a steam engine to clear it. The water rose through a bore-hole only three inches in diameter, at a rate of nearly one foot per hour and the result looked promising. Smith now proposed that further excavation below the rock should take place, to collect water from the streams flowing through the fissures and to provide reservoirs to ensure a regulated supply to the canal, as needed. Smith preserved no documents recording whether this work was carried out. Possibly because the oolitic rock was only twenty-one feet (6·4m) thick, the water supply was later found to be very limited and in 1820 the experiment was abandoned.

In 1817, Smith was called to East Anglia, where he surveyed and prepared plans for a joint river and canal project along the valley of the Waveney, from Diss to Bungay. From Yarmouth, he observed widespread flooding of the Yare, the Thurn and the Waveney, and expressed disappointment that, twelve years after the sea defences had been completed, little had been done in the much simpler task of improving the drainage of fresh water.

He then went up to Yorkshire to survey for a new canal between Knottingley, on the River Aire, and Doncaster on the Don, with a branch down the River Went. He worked intermittently on this project over the next two years, and drew up a plan for the *Proposed Aire and Dunn Canal to drain the contiguous lands and to shorten and connect the present navigation.* It was signed: *William Smith, 1819.* In the bottom right-hand corner is a note to the effect that the map was 'drawn on stone by J. Phillips.' However, when the enabling Bill was brought before Parliament, it was defeated by the strenuous opposition of the Aire and Calder Navigation Company. While Smith was in the area, he got to know well the lias coast at Whitby and Scarborough, and the local limestones, clays and sandstones, together with the Lower Permian red beds known as the Rotliegende (from which today much of northern Europe's natural gas is extracted). He added all his new-found knowledge to the map, based on the large *County Survey* of Jeffreys, that he had started colouring in 1803. This was eventually published in 1820 and 1821 on Cary's four-sheet map.

He visited many parts of the country over the next three years, including frequent trips to the collieries in the Forest of Dean. He constantly added to his maps any new observations and drew plans and sections of many coal-mines. One in particular is of interest, because it showed the winding course across the coal-beds of the 'Great Horse'. This is an area in which coal should have been found, but for some peculiar reason was missing. It was thought that it must have been a flowing water-course through the peat bog from which the coal was formed that washed it away in this particular place.

Between 1816 and 1819, Smith published a series of works entitled *Strata Identified by Organized Fossils, containing Prints on Coloured Paper of the most Characteristic specimens in each Stratum.* It consisted of numerous drawings of fossils printed on nineteen differently-tinted papers, corresponding to some degree with the natural colours of the strata. Only four of the seven proposed editions appeared. Back in 1808, Smith had approached James Sowerby, whom he knew to be preparing *The Mineral Conchology of Great Britain*, asking him if he would engrave the plates for this work, but it seems that Sowerby did not think it an economic proposition. Partly because Smith was fully occupied with other business, several years elapsed without any progress. In 1813, Sowerby agreed to prepare the plates, if Smith found another publisher to carry the financial risk. He did so, but it came to nothing. Sowerby eventually agreed to publish the work himself, after William Lowndes, M.P., First Commissioner for the Affairs of Taxes, a good friend of Smith and one of his former employers, advanced £50 to pay for the first edition. However, the cost of production, estimated at £50 per title, plus the expenses of publication deducted from the gross sale price of £95 15s (assuming all 250 copies were sold), left little room for profit. Smith received nothing from the sales until 1832. Summarising the country's rocks and their localities, Smith goes on:

> The Method of knowing the Substrata from each other by their various substances imbedded, will consequently shew the difference in their soils. All this is attainable by rules the most correct, and easily learnt, and also the simplest and most extensive that can well be devised; for by the help of organised Fossils alone, a science is established with characters on which all must agree, as to the extent of the strata in which they are imbedded, those characteristics are universal; and a knowledge of them opens the most extensive sources of information, without the necessity of deep reading, or the previous acquirement of difficult arts .... Fossil Shells had long been known to the curious, collected with care, and preserved in their cabinets, along with other rarities of nature, without any apparent use. That to which I have applied them is new, and my attention was first drawn to them, by a previous discovery of regularity in the direction and dip of the various Strata in the hills around Bath.'
>
> The northernmost of the three principal portions, North and South of the Humber, is small, long, and narrow, lying low, and as yet little known for organized fossils, except large bones washed out of the crumbly cliffs of Holderness, which correspond with those washed out of similar cliffs on the coast of East Norfolk, Suffolk, Essex, East Kent, and South Hants.

As the Public can only judge, partially of
these labours, by the small proportion
of my Documents yet before them
others who may be engaged in fol-
-lowing out & correcting what they
suppose to be imperfect might
spare much of that trouble if
they knew the extent and accuracy
of my yet unpublished Papers.

Wm Smith
Civil Engineer

15 Buckingham Street
York Buildings
London

June 1818

29. Smith's handwriting, 1818.

Some twenty-seven fossil species were first given names by Smith in his *Strata identified by Organized Fossils* (it should be noted that Linnaeus had introduced binomial nomenclature in 1749 and Smith had adopted it). They are listed in Appendix 1.

In 1817, Smith and Phillips worked their way southwards along the Yorkshire coast from Whitby to try to throw light on the geology of the county. They were able to use their knowledge of fossils to distinguish unfamiliar strata. The multiple exposures along the shore were, of course, much more useful than the small number inland. In Whitby Smith met John Bird, whom he had first encountered in 1813. Bird had considerable knowledge of the local rocks and fossils and was a most useful ally. When Smith and Phillips reached Scarborough, they visited Thomas Hinderwell and John Hornsey, who both had fine collections of fossils. For want of a stratigraphic framework into which to arrange the specimens, their collections were displayed together in groups of similar species, described but not named. Nevertheless, they were most valuable to Smith and his nephew in providing detail on their geological map. That in turn helped them not only for pure interest but commercially, when it came to advising landowners about the siting of quarries and wells and the best crops to sow. They returned to the Yorkshire coast in 1820 to finalise a geological map of the county, which was eventually published in 1821. Phillips drew Smith's attention to errors he had made in the situations of the Inferior and Coralline Oolites and the Calcareous Grit. Smith also confused the Lias Alum Shale with the Oxford Clay and this misidentification was very soon noted and publicised by knowledgeable members of the Geological Society. The York philosophers were encouraged to start their own researches and to expand existing knowledge in the new science. Phillips identified three fossils found by Smith near Scarborough as being characteristic of the Kelloways rock, and this helped to differentiate between the Oolites, but having been caught out before, Smith was cautious. However, he accepted the interpretation some three years later. Although he did not seem overconcerned about it, his reputation was important, because upon it depended his income.

Also in 1817, Smith published *A Stratigraphical System of Organized Fossils with reference to the specimens of the Original Geological Collection in the British Museum: explaining their state of preservation and their use in identifying the British Strata,* compiled from his own collection, now in the British Museum of Natural History. There were careful notes of the localities in which the specimens had been found, and he added coloured tables, the first of their kind ever published, showing the geological distribution of particular groups. The Introduction states:

> This novel and interesting description of near seven hundred species of Fossil Shells, Zoophites, and other organized Fossils, found in England and Wales, and collected in identification of the Strata, refers particularly to the specimens of a geological collection deposited in the British Museum. On the specimens, Roman capitals mark the genus, - the figures 1, 2, 3, &c, refer to the species. - and the small letters, a, b, c, &c., to the localities or sites in the Strata.
>
> This copious reference to the stratum which contains the Fossils, to the particular site therein whence obtained, and to the individual specimens in the collection, which is intended to be publicly exhibited in the British Museum, seemed to render figures of them unnecessary; especially as reference is constantly made to another work of the Author's now publishing by Mr. Sowerby, which consists chiefly of engravings [*Strata identified by Organized Fossils*]; and as further reference is also made to the numerous figures of Sowerby's *Mineral Conchology.*
>
> The virtuoso will therefore now enter upon the study and selection of Organised Fossils with the twofold advantage of amusement and utility. The various component parts of the soil, and all the

> subterraneous productions of his estate become interesting objects of research; the contents of quarries, pits, wells, and other excavations, hitherto thought unworthy of notice, will be scrupulously examined.
>
> This particular branch of geology has already proved that a large portion of the earth once teemed with animation, and that the animals and plants thus finely preserved in the solid parts of the earth's interior, are so materially different from those now in existence, that they may be considered as a new creation, or rather as an undiscovered part of an old creation. They are chiefly submarine, and as they vary generally from the present inhabitants of the sea, so at separate periods of the earth's formation they vary as much from each other; insomuch that each layer of these fossil organised bodies must be considered as a separate creation; or how could the earth be formed *stratum super stratum*, and each abundantly stored with a different race of animals and plants. Surely these innumerable and finely organized fossils are not the sports of nature placed there to excite the attention of the idly curious, but they must, like the other works of the great Creator, have their use.
>
> The chief object of this work being to show the utility of organized Fossils in identifying the Strata, nothing further will be attempted in the systematic arrangement than is necessary to make the subject intelligible; and the numerous useful and interesting deductions thence resulting will more appropriately follow than precede the regular description of them in the order of the strata. *The Term* 'Organized Fossils' *is generally applied to all fossil matter that has a relation to the form of any organized body, either animal or vegetable.* These substances are also called *'Fossils', 'Petrifactions,' and 'Organic Remains'.*

There follows a *Geological Table of British Organized Fossils, which identify the courses and continuity of the Strata in their order of superposition; as originally discovered by W. Smith, Civil Engineer; with reference to his Geological Map of England and Wales*. A note at the bottom of the Table states:

> From the re-examination of the Author's numerous Specimens in the arrangement of his Geological Collection in the British Museum and his subsequent observations, this list of the Strata has been improved and his future exertions will be in proportion to the encouragement which he receives from the Public.

By all accounts this was very little!

The Table begins with London Clay and its fossils, followed by similar treatment for eighteen further strata. Then comes a *Table of Echini*, which occupy eight strata. In his *Memoirs,* John Phillips claims that these tables were 'the first of the kind ever published'.

A *Table of the Distribution of Ammonites, drawn up by John Phillips, under the direction of William Smith, in 1817* was not published until Phillips gave details of it to the Annual General Meeting of the Geological Society on 17 February 1860. A footnote states that 'The Table was drawn up previous to the publication, in 1817, of the *Stratigraphical System of Organized Fossils'* [which contains a few more names of Ammonites - some proposed by Smith, e.g. *A. Calix*, now called *A. Blagdeni*].

John Cary now began publishing a series of county maps and geological sections, similarly coloured to the great map but more meticulously drawn with regard to the boundaries of the strata. In all, twenty-one maps were produced. There was a large one of Yorkshire in four sheets. They were issued in two series. The rationale behind the first was 'to point out those places where Coal and other valuable Minerals are likely to be found.' The second showed 'the Situation of the best Materials for Building, making Roads, constructing Canals etc.' *A Geological Table of British Organized Fossils*, measuring 16½inches by 14½inches (43 by 37cm) and similar to that included in Smith's *Stratigraphical System* was published, and included a chart with the beds numbered, showing exactly which ones occur in each county. Forty counties and North and South Wales were covered.

Part of this series was one of the most remarkable of Smith's publications, a *Geological Section from London to Snowdon, showing the Varieties of the Strata, and the correct altitudes of the Hills. By William Smith, Civil Engineer 1817. Coloured to correspond with his Geological Map of England and Wales. The numbers refer to the geological table by the same author. Various heights of hills, etc., are given by means of a 'scale of feet'.* On the left margin of the chart is written:

> THIS SECTION shows correctly the relative altitudes and general features of the Country along the Road through the Places marked on it forming an Epitome of BRITISH GEOLOGY, naturally and distinctly divided into seven Classes, four principal Ranges of High Ground and three of low. The hills thus appear to be chiefly composed of rocky and hard Strata & the Vallies of lax and soft. The Elevations above the Level of the Sea are obtained from the Trigonometrical Survey. Several distant Eminences are shown in the respective Ranges of Hills. The Contour is unavoidably distorted from the Necessity of representing the Distances and Altitudes by different Scales. Some Strata in the Series which are obscure upon this Road are very distinct upon others. Further elucidation of the Strata discovered and traced by W. Smith are given in his other works.

Towards the end of 1818, Smith went back to the village of his birth, and revisited the spots where he remembered finding his first fossils near Churchill Mill. While he had spent all that he had earned on what he deemed a public service, he found one of his brothers had become prosperous. The common

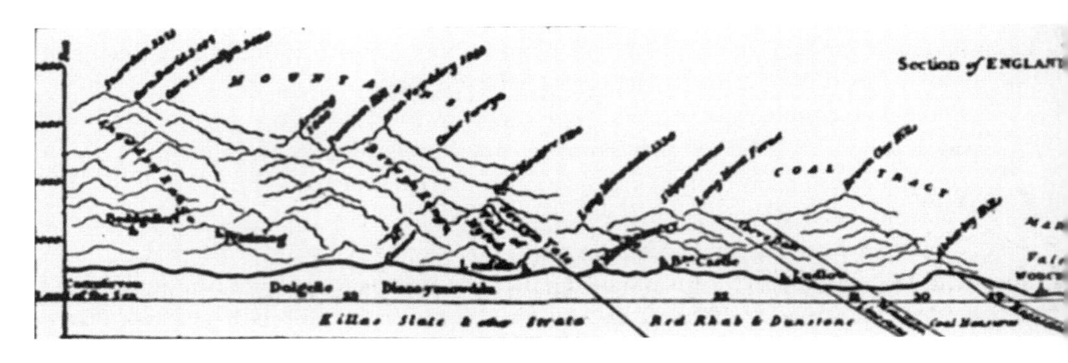

28. Smith's Geological Section from London to Snowdon, 1817.

land had been enclosed in 1787, but many of the lighter diversions of the villagers, such as the wake known as the 'Whitsun-ale' remained. Local people could remember the digging up of iron pyrites (which they called 'golden stones') to make a pond at Sarsden, a mile to the south, and Warren Hastings had returned from India to supervise the ornamental planting of his family estate, Daylesford, 2½ miles to the north-west.

On 15 April 1819, Smith was visited in London by Peter Browne, representing the Government of the United States of America. Browne had been commissioned to employ a canal engineer to investigate the practicability of by-passing falls on seven navigable rivers in North Carolina. Smith returned the visit two days later at Browne's lodgings at 35 Leicester Square, where they went into the project in detail. However, following overtures by his friends, James Brogden, M.P., and the eccentric John (Mad Jack) Fuller of Brightling in Sussex, Smith declined Browne's offer. Had he accepted it, he would, no doubt, have taken John Phillips with him, which as it turned out, would have been a great loss to the country.

The year 1819 saw the production of a geological map on a smaller scale (fifteen miles to the inch), 'intended as an Elementary Map for those commencing the study of Geology.' The beds are coloured as usual, but in the space occupied by the North Sea are *A List of Canals & Navigable Rivers shewing the principal articles of Mineral Tonnage* [including a list of 100 canals, and 97 rivers] *and Railways* [numbering 20]. The 'Articles of Tonnage' are:

> principally Coal, Iron and Ironstone, but include Granite, Lime, Limestone, Flagstone, Stone, Slate, Lead China Stone, Sea Sand, Flints, Firestone, Fuller's Earth, Ore, Gravel, Culm, Mountsorrel Stone, Flags, Paving stone, Defence Sea Beach, Pottery, Gypsum, Fire Clay, Potter's Clay, Sea Sand, Copper Ore, Salt, Salt Rock, Freestone, Gun Flints, Reach, Oysters, Millstones, Shell Sand,

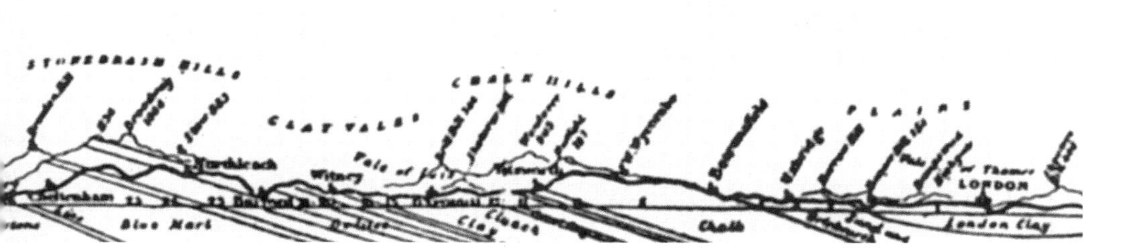

(From a reproduction in The Philosophical Magazine, January 1833)

> Cannel, Manganese, Chalk, Roadstone, Pipe Clay, Loam, Ochre, Marble, Powder, Grindstones.

Smith also made a start on a *New Geological Atlas of England and Wales*, of which six parts were published, the last in 1824. The first part covered Norfolk, Kent, Wiltshire and Sussex; the second Gloucester, Berkshire, Surrey and Suffolk. The third edition featured Oxford, Buckinghamshire, Bedford, and Essex, while part four, which appeared in 1821, contained a map of Yorkshire in four sections. Part five dealt with Nottingham, Leicester, Huntingdon and Rutland, and part six Cumberland, Durham, Northumberland and Westmorland. Phillips records that 'other parts to complete this work were left in a state of forwardness.' All these maps contained more detail than Smith's large one of 1815, showing that he had improved his knowledge in the intervening years.

The Yorkshire map Smith augmented was entitled *A New Map of Yorkshire, Divided into its Ridings and subdivided into Wapontakes, exhibiting Its Roads, Rivers, Parks, &c. By John Cary, Engraver. 1821.* Professor Judd reviewed it in the *Geological Magazine* in 1898 and commented:

> This is one of the finest of Smith's works. It is full of admirably worked out details. In the West Riding, the outcrops of the chief of the grit beds are represented on the map with their relations to the coal seams, and a fine vertical section of them is given; and in the north-east of the county, Smith clearly defines the estuarine strata of the Lower Oolites as follows: 'Sand Rock and Grit Freestone of the Moors, lying over the Alum Shale' (Upper Lias) 'and, in Scarborough Castle Hill, under the Oolite or Calcareous Freestone. A thin Coal in the cliffs is worked on the moors at Danby and other places.' In this work we see the fruits of Smith's

> residence at Scarborough, which commenced in the year 1820. Each outcrop is coloured, with a tablet index, and the 'Whinstone Dyke' is featured. On the Holderness cliffs is printed: 'Here stood Auburn, which was washed away by the Sea'; 'Hartburn, washed away'; 'Hyde, washed away'.

In the same year, Smith issued five charts, the first in two parts: *GEOLOGICAL VIEW AND SECTION OF NORFOLK* and *GEOLOGICAL VIEW AND SECTION THROUGH SUFFOLK TO ELY.*

The cost of publishing his Geological Sections was the final straw in Smith's burden of debt and, in 1819, he was obliged to leave his house in London and sell all his possessions, including his books. John Farey kindly secured his papers, drawings and maps, or these would have gone too. Charles Conolly was the creditor who foreclosed on Smith, who actually spent ten weeks in the King's Bench Prison for debt. He was forced to sell his beloved Tucking Mill. Smith and Phillips went to live in the north. Having rather more leisure time than previously, Smith set out in December 1819 to walk with his nephew, John Phillips, from Lincolnshire to Wiltshire. Noting the geology as usual, collecting fossils and sketching parts of the road, they passed through Rutland, Northampton, Bedford and Oxford, eventually to reach Swindon. They went on to London, stopping at Oxford, where Smith met William Buckland for the first time, a Reader in Mineralogy at the University who had been honoured by being elected a Fellow of the Royal Society in 1818.

6

'The Father of English Geology'

Smith's services to science were first recognised publicly in 1818 by Dr. Fitton, in an article entitled *Notes on the progress of English Geology* in the *Edinburgh Review*. He wrote:

> A map may not, at first sight, appear to come within the scope of our publication; but the performance now before us ... has more than ordinary claims upon the attention of the public ... It is the first work of the kind that has ever appeared in England; and it is the production, after the labour of more than twenty years, of a most ingenious man, who has been singularly deficient in the art of introducing himself to public notice.

For some years, Smith had no regular home but travelled to cover his professional engagements or his geological investigations. The fact that Smith had a wife is mentioned for the first time in his nephew's *Memoirs of William Smith,* in his narrative of the year 1820, when her husband took her to Scarborough 'in hopes to soothe her mental aberration, which became very manifest in this year.' Research has shown that he probably married in 1808, as his wife Mary Ann is first referred to in his diary for August 1809, when he was forty and she nineteen. Unfortunately, no diary for 1808 (the likely year of their marriage) survives, and at least four researchers have failed to find any parish record entries referring to it. A description much later, in 1824, portrays her as:

> an eccentric little round-faced woman of a small and somewhat stunted figure, oddly altered, with her cheeks rouged to the highest point of which they were capable. She was occasionally subject to violent outbursts of temper, which for a time disturbed the even tenor of her husband's ways.

Two and a half years after her husband's death, she was admitted on 15 February 1842, to the County Lunatic Asylum at Bootham, just outside York. She was patient number 3860, and was described in the Admission Book as Mary A. Smith of Scarborough, aged 'about 50', state of mind 'tractable'. In the parallel Register of Cases she is shown as a widow, and under the 'occupation' described as 'Lady'. Under 'by whom sent' it says 'Her Nephew' (presumably John Phillips). The duration of her disease is noted as 'several years' and the figure 18 and comment 'from 35' have been added. Under 'state of mind' she is said to be 'irritable'. Added in pencil above is 'monomania' and under apparent cause it says 'Nimphomania' [sic]. She died on 27 June 1844, at the age of fifty-two, according to the Register 'from fever accompanied by Effusion on Brain.' There is no record of her having been admitted to and discharged from the Asylum, nor the Quaker-run York Retreat, earlier than 1842, even though she had a long history of mental illness. Presumably she was looked after in a domestic environment, firstly by her husband and latterly by John Phillips.

Yorkshire was attractive for Smith and Phillips – it was well away from London, where Smith had run into financial difficulties, and it was a county full of rich landowners needing their advice for improving the productivity of their agriculture and the exploitation of their mineral wealth. Interest in geology was burgeoning through the newly-formed philosophical societies. Smith became very fond of Scarborough. In 1820, there was a proposal that a museum be founded there. Smith attended a meeting at the house of Dr. John Dunn to discuss it. Also present were Dunn's medical partner, William Travis, a keen botanist, William Bean, the town's most noted naturalist, and the owner of the county's most important fossil collection, Thomas Hinderwell. Unfortunately, Hinderwell's collection had already been willed to his nephew, Thomas Duesbery, a solicitor in the town, and it was not available as a basis for a new museum. Nothing came of the idea until the Scarborough Philosophical Society was established some years later.

Early in 1821, Smith and his nephew walked through the coal-producing districts of the West Riding. They were looking to establish the true general order of the coal beds, ironstone courses and characteristic rocks. Their findings were reflected in detail on the Yorkshire map. The first page of Smith's notes indicates the kind of information they were seeking:

> 4th April, 1821. - Walked westward by Barlby and Warmsworth to Sprotburgh Ferry, and thence by Cadeby over the verge of the magnesian limestone there. Cadeby is so very ill supplied with water, that those who hold the pump-handle must frequently wait some time till the niggard stream furnishes its scanty supply. There is, however, a pool in the place, and some springs appear above the edge of the hill which, as at Micklebring, is kept by the purple sandstone. Several yew trees mark its course. Before we arrive at the mill on the

> Dearn, some clay ground and dark shades in the soil indicate the outcrop of the uppermost workable vein of coal. Melton Hall, to the right on the edge of the limestone, is very conspicuous. We now ascend a bold bank, and at the junction of the Barmborough and Melton road, wind round a sudden swell of limestone and sandstone, whose outcropping beds form around the face a series of natural entrenchments clothed with wood. Beyond this hill the ridge recedes from our road and leaves a broad vacancy, wherein we descry a coal-pit. To our left is Barmborough Grange, standing on detached sandstone.

In a footnote, Phillips says:

> On this map, for the first time, an attempt, by no means unsuccessful, was made to divide and colour the great coal district into groups of rocks and shales; the course of the 'Pontefract Rock,' 'new red sandstone,' or 'rothe liegende' was traced out, and the magnesian limestone divided into its component members. The first copies of this map have one grand error in the north-eastern moorlands, which are represented to consist of oolitic strata not lower than the 'Clunch (Oxford) clay', whereas the great subjacent shale is lias. This, however, Mr. Smith quickly discovered and rectified.

To help his uncle, Phillips made a number of other journeys from Doncaster, to collect enough supplementary material for the geological map of Yorkshire to be completed. It was published in the summer of 1821, in four sheets.

In order to finish more of the series of county maps, Smith and Phillips spent the rest of 1821 on long, hard trips. They worked on parallel lines across the countryside, Phillips occasionally rejoining his uncle to bring him his reports. Between them, they covered over 2000 miles in six months. They took the opportunity to visit the rich quarries of Canwick, near Lincoln, to collect more fossils, then went on a very thorough journey of observation through the coal-fields of Nottingham and Derby, into Yorkshire and Lancashire and on to the Lake District. Smith was soon able to publish maps of Cumberland, Westmorland and Lancashire, together with the best produced so far, Cary's *Sheet Map of the Lakes*, coloured in September 1821.

The pair proceeded to explore thoroughly the Lake District and the region immediately to the south of it, asking local people about the history of the lead mines. They then set out to cross the Pennines and the southern part of the Cheviots by different routes, meeting in Durham, where they stayed for a while. Next, they turned south by roughly parallel routes through the limestone and millstone grit of Durham and Yorkshire, ending up in Leeds. Here, Smith was introduced to the most active members of the recently-formed Philosophical Society. On 16 November 1821, he attended their lecture on the place in nature of the Hippocampus, the 'sea horse' at the Leeds Philosophical and Literary Society. He volunteered to address them the following day on the subject of geology. He illustrated his talk with his own map, describing the varied stratification of Yorkshire and occasionally extending it to the whole country. He also made some useful suggestions on the arrangement of the geological specimens in the Society's museum. This, probably Smith's first lecture in Yorkshire, was very well received.

He continued to record observations of the local stratification. Phillips then drew up a map combining all his results.

After this, they set out to walk from Leeds to Nottingham with the intention of seeing out the winter there. However, Smith made a short visit to London and met by accident Colonel Braddyll who asked him to make a general survey of his estates in Lancashire, Cumberland and Durham, with a view to finding copper ore in the limestone. Surprisingly, many lumps of copper had been found in narrow crevices in the limestone and in what was then thought to be the 'diluvial' gravel which covered it.

Colonel Braddyll owned some 700 acres (283 hectares) of poor land on the limestone at Haswell, a small village to the east of the city of Durham. He had been advised that the land was of little value and that there were unlikely to be any minerals worth exploiting. Other landowners in the area had been advised by coal prospectors from Newcastle that, if there were any coal under their property, it would not be of marketable quality and not worth the cost of exploitation. Observing from the situation of the neighbouring coal district that the limestone sat unconformably above the coal, Smith inferred that good seams of coal could be found at an attainable depth at Haswell. He was able to convince Braddyll and after some years of difficulty the Colonel established the highly profitable South Hetton Colliery.

Smith stayed for some time at Kirkby Lonsdale, twelve miles south-east of Kendal near the Cumbria/Lancashire border. The area was of particular interest to him, because five distinct strata crop out there, and they are heavily folded. Here he derived great pleasure from meeting, for the first time, Professor Adam Sedgwick, to within a day sixteen years his junior. Sedgwick had been elected to the Woodwardian Chair of Geology at Cambridge in the summer of 1818, although he had at the time little knowledge of the subject. Having received the honour, he determined to convert the Chair from the sinecure that it had been, to the leading position in a new discipline. He studied geology earnestly and spent the summer of 1816 in Derbyshire working on it, giving his first lecture at Easter 1819. He had come across to Kirkby Lonsdale from Teesdale, where the stone-masons, recognising from his hammer that he had the same interests, pointed Smith out to him. They walked together for a short distance along the road towards Kendal, and Smith probably showed him the greywacke quarries in which he had recently found organic remains.

Smith was able to complete his maps of Westmorland and Lancashire and significantly improve the one of Yorkshire, by introducing the Silurian slates near the summits of Ingleborough and Graygarth. This is probably the map that he presented to the Yorkshire Philosophical Society in 1826. With his nephew, he went out on frequent rambles, collecting fossils from several distinct beds from slate to limestone, and sketching waterfalls. They made a visit to Hesket Newmarket, twelve miles north-west of Penrith, and spent two to three months there, looking at both active and abandoned lead and copper mines. They remarked upon the extraordinary variety of minerals in the veins and rocks and the area's resemblance to the mineral-rich regions of Cornwall. In January 1823, at home in Kirkby Lonsdale, they set up a small smelting furnace to carry out experiments to investigate the crystalline structure and chemical composition of their samples.

Smith was so isolated in the Lune valley, that he only heard of an urgent official request for his services as a mineral surveyor in Russia when it was too late, otherwise, according to his nephew's opinion, he would probably have gone. However, in his *Literary Recollections* (1830), the Rev. Richard Warner says:

> I had the pleasure of knowing Mr. Smith well: and the advantage of occasionally deriving information from him; it gives me pleasure to reflect that I had an opportunity of making a slight return for his kindness, by procuring an offer to be made to him, which, had it been accepted, would certainly have given him independence; and probably led to wealth and honour. The circumstance ought not to be concealed, as it reflects much credit on the character of Mr. Smith. When Count Orloff was in England, attached to the Count's suite, and placed under his protection by the Emperor Alexander, was Dr. Hamel, a Russian physician, now well known to all the scientific institutions in Europe. Some time after Count Orloff had quitted Bath, Dr. Hamel was commissioned by the Emperor, to find out and engage some English practical mineralogist, who would be competent to direct and superintend the coal-works, in one of the southern provinces of the Russian empire. Dr. Hamel applied to me for information on the subject; and I immediately recommended Mr. Smith as a person every way eligible for such a situation. He was then in London: I obtained his address, and sent it to Dr. Hamel. A correspondence commenced between them, and offers of the most flattering description were made by the Emperor's agent. But Mr. Smith was a patriot, and unwilling to sell his valuable services to a foreign country. He was engaged too, at the moment, in arranging the minerals for the British Museum; and promises were made to him, if he would forego the Russian offer, of permanent and lucrative employment in his own country. In a short time Dr. Hamel

> announced to me and regretted Mr. Smith's final refusal. I know not whether these promises have been performed to Mr. Smith; if not, he has been treated unjustly, and the country deprived of services which might have been importantly useful to it.

Warner's version of what would seem to be the same story indicates the date to have been 1816, however, his nephew, who was after all living with him at the time, put it seven years later and with a different light on Smith's character. It would seem that Warner allowed his imagination to embellish his story.

In *Reminiscences of a Yorkshire Naturalist,* published in 1896 by William Crawford Williamson, we read:

> In 1824 my father [John Williamson, the first Curator of the Scarborough Museum] became personally acquainted with the great Father of Geology, William Smith, and with his subsequently distinguished nephew, the late Professor John Phillips. In 1826 Dr. Smith and his eccentric wife established themselves in our house, where they dwelt for a considerable time [two years] ..... One of the grandest figures that ever frequented Eastern Yorkshire was William Smith ..... My boyish reminiscences of the old engineer, as he sketched a triangle on the flags of our yard, and taught me how to measure it, is very vivid. The drab knee-breeches and grey worsted stockings, the deep waistcoat, with its pockets well furnished with snuff, of which ample quantities continually disappeared within the finely chiselled nostril, and the dark coat with its rounded outline and somewhat quakerish cut, are all clearly present in my memory. Spending the greater portion of his morning in writing, towards noon he would slowly wend his way to the museum, where he always found in my father a friend with whom to gossip about the rocks of the Cotswolds, the clays of Kimmeridge, or the drainage of the Eastern Fens. He would expound in a Coleridgean fashion his ideas of their relation to the strata of Yorkshire and of the other parts of England. His walking pace never varied, it was slow and dignified; he was usually followed a few yards in the rear by his rose-cheeked partner in life. We have a thousand times contemplated the fine old man, who, amid his favourite haunts, thus laid the foundations of geological science.

A resident of Kirkby Lonsdale, Edward Wilson wanted to provide for his town a better water supply from the local springs, and Smith was able to give him good advice as to how to go about it. Smith was introduced to a relative of Wilson, Dr. Matthew Allen of York, who on his return home, spoke of him to members of the recently-formed Yorkshire Philosophical Society. The result was an invitation from their President, the Reverend William Vernon, to deliver a series of lectures on geology in York. Although he had given an impromptu talk to the Philosophical and Literary Society at Leeds in 1821, he had never given a formal lecture before. He had certainly been talking about geology for many years to anyone who would listen, so he immediately accepted.

He coloured new maps, drew new sections and sent to his old friend, the Rev. Benjamin Richardson, for some drawings from his collection of fossils to illustrate his lectures. He was warmly received, and introduced as 'a geologist of distinguished merit and reputation'. He began with an introduction to geology, pointing out that it was of universal interest and that there were plenty of facilities to study it in Britain. He emphasised its use for Man's convenience and illustrated this with maps and sections. He then looked at the termination of strata in the sea and their connection with those in adjacent countries. He discussed features of the sea-shore and of inland formations. He went on to deal with the principles of natural drainage, the site of settlements, their water supplies, the nature of the soils and how these affected agriculture.

Further lectures covered strata, their identification with fossils and their relative antiquity, the variations in the strata, unconformities, faults, dykes and mineral veins. Next, he dealt with the geology of Yorkshire and went on to show the practical advantages and the beneficial application of geology in agriculture, pottery and brickmaking, the selection of grindstones, mining, and quarrying for building stone. Finally, he reviewed the subject, explaining the deposition of sediments, considering the evidence for a change of climate and discussing the effects of what he thought of then as the Deluge - the rounding of rocks and fossils by flowing water. He also looked at evidence of the antediluvian inhabitants of Earth.

John Phillips comments in his *Memoirs* (p.109):

> A certain abstractedness of mind, generated by long and solitary meditation, a habit of following out his own thoughts into new trains of research, even while engaged in explaining the simplest facts, continually broke the symmetry of Mr. Smith's lectures. Slight matters, things curious in themselves but not clearly or commonly associated with the general purpose of the lecture, swelled into excrescences, and stopped the growth of parts which were more important in themselves, or necessary to connect the observations into an intelligible and satisfactory system. But there was a charm thrown over these discourses by the novelty and appropriateness of the diagrams and modellings which exemplified the arrangement of rocks, the total absence of all technical trifling from the explanations, and the simplicity and earnestness of the man.

It was a course of lectures in Scarborough Town Hall, given by Smith assisted by his nephew in the summer of 1824, that inspired a surge in fossil-collecting. They were delighted to renew their acquaintance with the town, with its geological peculiarities, to meet old friends and to make new ones, particularly John Williamson and William Bean, both established collectors. This triggered off the foundation of two museums and sparked a general interest in geological research amongst the residents, which was most useful in developing understanding of the local strata and their fauna. The Scarborough Literary and Philosophical Society was established in spite of pressure from York, where the county society was anxious not to lose a rich source of fossils. It held its first meeting in 1827.

Smith wrote numerous papers on the local geology of Scarborough and gave a course of lectures to the Literary and Philosophical Society of Sheffield. Later in the year he also addressed a similar society in Kingston upon Hull. It was here that he expounded his interpolative approach based on the 'natural order of the strata, which probably never varies'. He said:

> We have only to find in any district of the Country some one well-known Stratum in the Series – observe its declination and escarpment – consider its relative situation or judge by Tables of Sections what other strata either higher or lower in the series should thereabout appear, then trace their outbursts in the order of succession, consider the width of ground occupied by each of their uncovered portions of the Strata and thus judge of their respective thicknesses and dip and so ascertain what is thereabout the internal structure of the Earth without penetrating the soil for that purpose.

This is not quite foolproof, as faults, recumbent folding and variations in lithology can cause errors, and Smith occasionally ran into such problems. He naturally found some strata more fossiliferous than others and used a combination of this factor and rock structure to provide a basis for identification.

In the early part of 1825, he pushed himself too hard, while examining a fault exposed on the north side of Castle Hill. He was confined to bed for several months with paralysis in his legs, but recovered slowly over the rest of the year. Whilst still incapable of walking, he addressed an audience numbering several hundred in Sheffield. With great patience and fortitude, Smith gave his lectures from a chair, somehow managing to make continuous references to his maps and numerous diagrams. While in Sheffield, he marshalled the mass of information he had gathered on the local coalfields. He then moved back to one of his former residences at Doncaster and put much hard work into the completion of the colouring of the large *Old Survey of Yorkshire*.

Roderick Impey Murchison served with the Duke of Wellington in Spain and Portugal. He left the army in 1816 to devote himself to geology. He later won the Copley Medal and became President of the British Association and of the Royal Geographical Society. When he visited the Yorkshire coast in 1826, he and Smith took a boat trip together from Scarborough to Whitby, which gave Smith the chance to point out to him the principal results of his comparison of the oolitic and lias strata of Yorkshire with those of the South of England. Murchison was also interested in establishing a connection between these Jurassic sediments and those at Brora, north-east of Dornoch on the coast of Highland. William Buckland and Charles Lyell, later to become Secretary to the Geological Society, had reasoned that the Brora seams were related to the plant-rich strata found on the coast at Whitby and Scarborough, and Murchison wanted to resolve the matter. He and Smith found themselves kindred spirits in respect of their attitude towards tireless and accurate work. In return for his helpfulness to Murchison, Smith shortly afterwards received the latter's memoir on the oolitic coalfield of Brora.

Also in 1826, Smith was visited by George William Featherstonhaugh, an American geologist who had crossed the Atlantic to study the construction of railways. His mother lived in Scarborough, and on visiting her, he took the opportunity to seek out Smith, who gave him details of the local Jurassic rocks and the fossils they contained. They walked together under the cliffs from Robin Hood's Bay to Whitby (about five miles). Featherstonhaugh suggested that Smith should name the various beds after their fossils, but the latter felt that geologists were not yet ready to accept such a nomenclature.

Smith had the occasional engagement in Scarborough, and was particularly interested in improving the water supply to the town, which received a large number of visitors each summer. Distant springs were out of the control of the town's authorities, but there was one small one on Falsgrave Moor, on the south-western outskirts. Smith attacked the problem from both ends. In the hillside he excavated a subterranean reservoir, which prevented loss of the scarce resource by evaporation, and in the town he constructed a large closed storage facility, which met the irregular demand of a varying population.

On 16 February 1827, Smith wrote from Scarborough to Sir John Vanden Bempde Johnstone, the owner of the nearby Hackness estate, who was anxious to help him in his work:

> Dear Sir John,
>
> Your brother having kindly favoured me with a call and your address, I beg leave to trouble you with some account of my proceedings during your absence. Ever since you left I have been almost daily employed by the commissioners for improving the town of Scarborough which suddenly became a truly improving place. The church is rising fast and a grand Spaw [spa] walk is forming at a great height along the frightful slope of the Spaw cliff close against the sea is already united by the immense platform required for constructing an Iron bridge of 5 arches 70 feet [21 metres] high. This grand project – suddenly started by subscribers from York, commenced in November and is rapidly proceeding.'

[This fine bridge, dated 1827, is still in use as a footway crossing Valley Road opposite the Rotunda Museum discussed below]. 'In addition to this stupendous bridge, there is already constructed what some have called 'a magnificent Reservoir' and in addition to this public work lighting the town with gas is seriously contemplated, my share in these great works though least seen is considered with great satisfaction, not the least useful. The Reservoir situate in the high part of the town, is I expect, the largest covered receptacle for water in England. It consists of a brick built cylinder sunk near 20 feet [6 metres] beneath the solid ground, 40 feet in diameter covered with a brick dome 40 feet span and 20 feet high, the whole of which immense arch consisting of 250 tons of brickwork turned without centreing or any woodwork to support the bricks, was closed the 20th. o-f January and we are now fast proceeding with the appendages requisite for filling it and a better distribution of water in the town. Nearly the whole of this building containing 120,000 bricks is underground or covered with a puddle and strong bank of earth giving it altogether the appearance of an immense Tumulus.

It will contain 4,000 Hogsheads [one hogshead = 52 imperial gallons = 239 litres] of water, but the other Reservoir (wholly unseen) made at my suggestion in the hills at a trifling expense to pen up in the rocks 5,000 Hogsheads of water is by far the most curious and perhaps the most useful practical hint hitherto deduced from Geology. It has so far exceeded our expectation of pinning up at the calculated height of four feet the above quantity that it has risen 12 feet and thence reasonably expected to produce in the next Summer fifteen thousand Hogsheads of water – So far, I think I was never in my life more usefully employed but the intricate calculations required in practical Hydraulics and the many complicated considerations thereof together with the superintendance of the works has retarded the progress of my intended publications on Yorkshire Geology – only the one sheet Geological map of the vicinity of Scarborough is complete. The six sheet (Cary's) new map of Yorkshire (as I shall now be more at liberty to complete the colouring) may shortly be published and notwithstanding my other engagements I have made considerable progress with my papers so that I think that the six sheet maps may be published for 3 guineas and the Geology of the County to accompany it for 2 guineas. I hope shortly to give you a better account of this work – and remain – most respectfully,

Your greatly obliged servant,
Wm. Smith.

The reservoir was situated in the Workhouse Yard (now Chapman's Yard, off North Street). Its purpose was to prevent waste from a newly-discovered spring, which ran continuously to the three public wells. At night, when these were not in use, they became full and the water overflowed. By diverting the spring into his new reservoir and putting a stop valve on the outflow, Smith was able to allow the level to rise when water was not in demand and provide a better and more economical supply when needed. (After 1884, the town Corporation, having invested heavily in new schemes, cut off the flow of free water to Smith's reservoir and the three town conduits, forcing the whole population to pay for its supply..)

Three weeks after his letter to Sir John was written, a paper by Smith was read to the Yorkshire Philosophical Society by its President, the Rev. William Vernon. It begins with a short treatise on the desirability of conserving water, and goes on:

> In the month of May last a small quantity was found to issue from a bore hole made several years since for draining the land. On cutting an open channel up to this, the discharge increased and at the depth of nine or ten feet amounted to twenty-four hogsheads per hour. This encouraged them to proceed; the channel under my direction was deepened four feet, when the discharge became for some time fifty or sixty hogsheads per hour.
>
> Suspecting from an intermediate and subsequent diminution that we had drawn off a confined stock of water, and that the regular run of the spring at the end of a dry summer might not be found sufficient, I suggested the propriety of damming up the produce of this spring for summer use, as the previous supply was more than sufficient for the town in winter.
>
> The circumstances were favourable for the purpose, as there was no other known issue of water from the rock in that hill, which is about a mile long, narrow on the top, and insulated in all the upper part of its stratification. The same rock is not opened or known anywhere else on these hillsides, but in a deep valley which separates the insular hill from the main and higher hill of Falsgrave Moor. In the upper end of that valley a spring was opened several years since in the same kind of rock, and was brought with a declivity of thirty or forty feet round the south end of the insulated hill, near to and high enough to run into the opening made to the new spring. This was sufficient to prove the general rise of the rock westerly in the base of the insular hill, and beneath an isthmus connected with the main ridge of Falsgrave Moor and Seamer Beacon. The rock in which the spring was found is a yellowish fine grained crumbly sandstone, in thick beds, with open irony joints, the same as in the cliff south of Scarborough Spa. From the quantity of carbonaceous matter in it, it is here called 'coaly grit.' This sandstone, with its

30. Part of a section of the strata around Scarborough, based on John Phillips's original mural, at the Scarborough Rotunda Museum.

overlying and alternating clays, is analagous in position to the clay and sand and sandstone between the cornbrash and great oolite rocks. At the depth of ten feet the rock was found covered with a regular clay about four feet thick; on this a mark of coal, and a thin bed of hard stone full of imperfect vegetable impressions; and up to the surface a very tenacious *slidden* clay. The rock was found, by boring through it, to be ten feet thick, lying on clay. The channel excavated up to the spring about thirty or forty yards long and fifteen feet deep, at the upper end was entirely in a very tenacious clay partly diluvial, with a few rounded stones in it deeply covered by slidden clay. Within four feet of the edge of the rock lay gravel (deeply covered also with slidden clay), consisting of large and small boulders of whinstone, granite, mountain-limestone, etc., which gravel, between the clay and the face of the rock tapered downward 'to nothing' in the bottom of the excavation.

About two yards within the edge of the rock (which was nearly as upright as the edge of a wall) a basin six feet in diameter and four feet deep was excavated, to receive the water flowing from the joints of the rock. Cast iron pipes branching from the main line of pipes were laid up to this basin, to receive the regular flow of the spring, which before the end of summer was reduced to less than six hogsheads per hour. The clay channel, in the bottom of which the

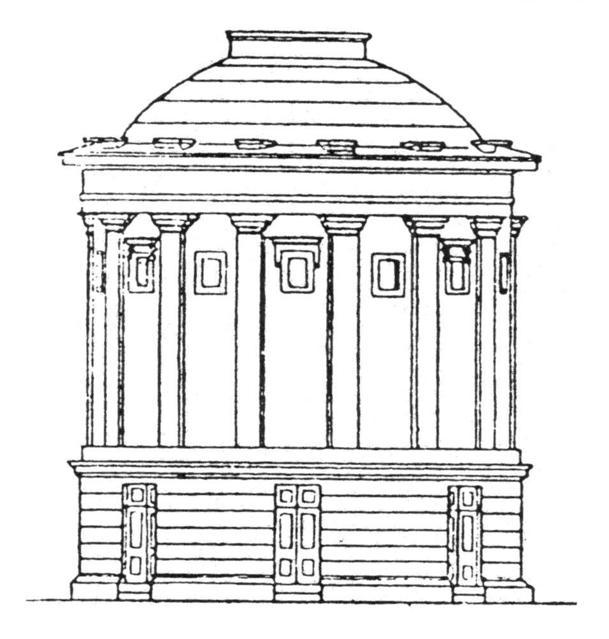

31. View of the Scarborough Museum as originally built. (From the Scarborough Philosophical Society's early reports)

pipes were laid, was refilled with clay and puddled, so that no water could pass from the rock but through the pipes. The end of the last pipe was closed, and a vertical aperture made for receiving the run of the spring. No further contrivance was required for stopping the water and damming it up in the rock, than an open vertical pipe, ground to fit tight into the aperture in the horizontal pipe, and this to a height of four feet was done by pieces of pipe, each a foot in length, tight-fitting one into another for the convenience of wholly or partially damming or drawing off the stored water as occasion might require; the water being allowed to run in at the top of the pipe.

After the rainy days in the beginning of November last, these short pieces of pipe were put in one after another, and found to dam up the water in the joints of the rock to the height of four feet, which from the quantity wasted last summer during the progress of the works was calculated to contain 5,000 hogsheads. The vertical pipe being since closed at the top (and lately also the main iron pipe), the whole of the water from those parts becomes forced in to the cavities of the rock, and now stands 14 feet deep at the spring, or ten feet higher than we calculated upon penning it; so that the subterraneous reservoir may contain 12,000 or 15,000 hogsheads of water. This will be ascertained in the summer as it is drawn down from time to time into the new arched reservoir in the town. This reservoir, formed of a brick cylinder 18 feet deep, sunk in the ground, and covered by a dome 40 feet span

> and 20 feet high, surrounded by a strong bank of earth, is calculated to contain 4,000 hogsheads.

In 1828, Smith settled at Hackness, about five miles north-west of Scarborough, where he had been given the position of land steward to Sir John Johnstone, which he held until 1834, continuing thereafter to be his scientific adviser. Sir John had been MP for Weymouth and Melcombe Regis, was elected Liberal MP for Yorkshire in 1830 and for Scarborough from 1832. Smith made his home in a house which was later to become Hackness Vicarage and he worked with his apprentice, Mr. Robert Turnbull, in his office in the west wing of the building.

Sir John found in Smith a man with both practical and theoretical knowledge when it came to the improvements in agriculture that he was seeking. He did his best to encourage Smith to publish more of his geological observations, offering financial support when necessary, but happy enough to impart them verbally to friends, Smith seemed loath to commit them to paper. He did, however, in 1829 or 1830, produce a detailed and accurate map of the Hackness estate. It was exhibited at the inaugural meeting of the British Association in York in 1831. Many valuable Johnstone family documents were lost in a fire in which the Hall was destroyed, and Smith's map may well have been among them. However, it seems that it was lithographed by W. Day of Lincoln's Inn Fields, London, and there is a record of a copy being given by Smith to the Yorkshire Philosophical Society in 1831, but it cannot now be found. Another copy came into the possession of the Scarborough Society around 1916. This was passed on to the Hull Municipal Museum, of which Thomas Sheppard was the Curator. It is entitled *Stratification in Hackness Hills By W. Smith 1832,* and is unfortunately uncoloured. It shows that Smith had a detailed knowledge of the estate covering close to twenty-five square miles (64 sq. km).

The first report of the Scarborough Society, founded in 1827, recorded that Smith's arrival in the district in 1820 had given 'a new feature to the study of geology, and an impulse to the student, which may be considered to have laid the basis of the Scarborough Museum.' At Smith's suggestion, the Museum was built as a circular structure with a cupola. It was was constructed with Hackness Stone, donated by Sir John Johnstone.and was thirty-two feet (9·75m) in diameter and thirty-six feet (11m) high. This, Smith thought, was most suitable for the display of fossils arranged on sloping shelves, one above the other, each shelf carrying those characteristic of its particular stratum. The building, at the north-east end of Valley Road, became known as the Rotunda. There was a version of Phillips's section of the strata of the Yorkshire coast 'as if viewed from the land', painted round the inside of the cupola, comfortably seen from the upper-level. It probably reflected the arrangement of the fossils displayed in the cases below, and was the work of a Mr. Todd, a painter and bookseller. In 1906 the original work was obliterated, but had first been carefully traced. It was reproduced in reverse, so that the sections appear as seen from the sea. It features seventeen different strata in Geological Survey colours.

Attached to the foundation stone of the Scarborough Museum was a brass plate reading:

This building, Erected for a Museum,
By Subscription of the Members of the
SCARBOROUGH PHILOSOPHICAL SOCIETY
was begun April 9, 1828.
The Principal Projectors were,
Sir John V.B. Johnstone, Bart., President;
Thomas Duesbery, Esq.,
who presented the collection of the late Thos. Hinderwell, Esq.;
Robert Tindall, Jun. Esq., Chairman of the
Building Committee;
John Dunn, Esq., Secretary:
William Smith, Esq., Geologist;
Mr. Bean and Mr. Williamson, Naturalists.

The museum was opened on 2 February 1830. The brass plate described above disappeared when the Rotunda was extended much later by the addition of wings on either side.

The glazed cases in the round upper-level room were constructed when the museum was being built in 1829. They now contain only a token display concerning Smith, comprising two geological maps, one of the Hackness Estate and the other of the Guisborough area including the coast, and a plaster bust of him, sculpted by Matthew Noble in 1848. The museum presently concentrates on social history; the natural history exhibits having been removed to the Woodend Museum, a short walk up Valley Road. There is sadly apparently nothing there which can be definitely identified as originating with Smith, though at the time of writing the Museum's store of specimens is in the process of being computerised and something may come to light.

In the latter part of 1830, the Editor of *The Whitby Repository* wrote to Smith, asking him for his comments on his idea that coal might be found near Robin Hood's Bay, based on an extraordinary dislocation of the strata shown in John Phillips's *Illustrations of the Geology of Yorkshire*. He was able to print what he termed Smith's 'elaborate and luminous communication':

> I perceive, by your letter, that your views of the probability of finding coal are not, like those of too many others, founded on the hope of finding it in shale or lias clay; but the question where to prick upon that intermediate range of the coal seams which may connect the coal-fields

15 Geology. 10] # Fine natural sections of all these strata in their corresponding order of superposition may be seen in Scarbro Castle hill & the cliffs between Filey & the latter place.

That geology is a science of unlimited extent & utility cannot be doubted but while geologists choose to be mannerists rather than correct imitators of nature some of its purposes remain unanswered. The application of this science to its most practical uses is nearly as herculean as its establishment.

Its uses in Agriculture are of the utmost importance to the country and therefore cannot be brought forward at a more convenient time than the present which calls for every stimulus to the skill and industry of the owners & occupiers of the soil. That a knowledge of Geology is the only infallible guide to determine correctly the value of Land was said 30 years since by that eminent land valuer, Davis of Wiltshire when the principles of the science were explained to him. To know what plants are best suited to the soil a knowledge of the varieties of soil is necessary which can only be obtained by an acquaintance with their subsoils & the strata upon which they rest & from which they are respectively formed.

Local circumstances and casual coverings of diluvial matter may make many shades of difference in the colour of a soil but with these allowances there certainly is no other method of obtaining such a general and practical knowledge of soils as by an acquaintance with the strata ~~the~~ which form them & upon which they rest. There may be considerable variety and great difference in the nature of a soil where no adventitious mixture occurs and this arises solely from a difference in the nature of the beds composing the thick stratum from which the soil is formed. These great varieties of soil varying according to the kind of stone upon which it reposes is well known to practical Farmers on the Hackness hills, and to most other occupiers of the same kind of land ~~from~~ thence to Hambleton. They all know there is a thin, dry, stony soil over the limestone, a deeper and more tenacious soil over the wallstone nearer the moors a range of free working yellowish sand land and poor, blackish, or grey sand upon the Moors

32. Smith's handwriting, 1830, part of his 'Memoir of the Stratification of Hackness Hills', 1829.

of Yorkshire and Durham, involves a great deal of deep geological consideration. My thoughts have often been turned to that important object; which, in a well chosen spot, is worthy of a national experiment. We know that all the beds of coal and their accompaniments, in the West Riding, sink under the Magnesian limestone in the vicinity of Abberford, much in the same manner as they rise from beneath the same kind of limestone at Ferry-Hill, in Durham; but the limestone being, in both cases, an unconformable covering, we have no clue from the Upper strata to the range of the coal seams between those two very distant parts. From the east and west range in the northernmost coals in Yorkshire, and a similar range in the southernmost coals in Durham, and from intermediate borings which I am acquainted with, I am satisfied that the coals do not range under an unconformable cover, through the low ground, in a straight line between those two places; and if they range in a curving line under the high land of the eastern moors, it is there impossible to get down to them. It seems unlikely, from various circumstances I can enumerate, both in Yorkshire and Durham, that a line curving eastward less than a semicircle, will never unite the coal-fields in question; and, as the greater part of this line passes under enormously thick piles of strata, mostly in very high ground, the only chances there are of finding coal at any great distance from those two coal-fields, are on the sea shore; and the best of all these, as I have long thought, is in Robin Hood's Bay. The magnesian limestone, if it could be found would not be worth getting by a pit in the Bay; and if coals can be found it would be well if the red marl could be sunken through without it, which I have reason to expect, or at least that it may be thin. It is a rock that varies much in thickness, and in the southern parts becomes extinct. The red marl, which is an unconformable cover to coal, of least extent in those parts, is sunken through, at all the pits, from 10 to 30 fathoms in thickness; this, like the limestone, varies much in thickness, and there are circumstances attending it which lead me to think it may not be very thick in some parts of the North Riding.

Nearly forty years since, I lived amongst coal-pits, commonly sunken through the lias and the red marl, and some of them through superincumbent beds as high in the series as the inferior oolite. We know that the alum shale or lias clay, and some of the other strata in these eastern moorlands, are of extraordinary thickness; but there is no reason to believe that the red marl, and especially the beds below it, which have no relation to those above, are thereabout thicker than usual.

A number of Smith's papers were passed down through his pupil, Robert Turnbull, via his daughters, the Misses A. and E. Turnbull and his grandson Mr. S.P. Turnbull, who gave them to the Scarborough Society. One was an essay in manuscript dated February, 1831 and entitled *Agriculture*; the following is part of it:

Grass cannot be prudently stored either for Summer or Autumn use: for the Farmer who does not eat his grass in Summer as fast as it grows, loses much of what the land would produce; and he that leaves it late on the ground for Autumn use, in what is called 'fogg', [long grass left standing in winter] wastes much thereof, and makes his grass-land coarse. Therefore, he that would farm grass-land to

> the greatest advantage, must either keep it through the Winter, or lay in as much stock as will eat down all the SUMMER grass on his pastures, as fast as it grows; and also as much cattle as will well eat down in the Autumn all the after-grass on the land that he mows. This is the only way to keep grass-land fine, and in good condition, and free from moss, weeds, and bad grasses; but many may think this would be going too *near the wind*, and that their stock would be likely to suffer from shortness of grass in dry seasons. It may be so where the farmer has none but grass-land, but this ought not to be the case upon any Farmer, for on no account, whatever, should the provision for these casualties be sought for in grass-land. The casualties of a dry Summer, and of occasional wants of keep, should be provided for in that part of the Farm which is cultivated, where such crops as Tares, Rye, &c., can be gotten up high enough to cover the ground before dry weather commences, and thus insure their growth. It is well known that winter Tares & Rye, sown early enough, can be cut and served out to Stock to the greatest advantage in the dryest Summer; and at all times they make the best of all provisions for the latter part of Spring, or the beginning of Summer, when Farmers are in more danger of injuring their grass-land by hard and too early stocking, than at any other time of the year. These and every other kind of early crop, which can be cut green, or in case of excess, for that purpose may be cut for Hay, or ripened for seed, should be grown in sufficient quantity upon every Farm. In this way the casualties of a dry Summer, & the wants of the latter part of Spring, may be certainly and profitably provided after Swedish Turnips, Carrots, and other roots are consumed. These two kinds of food for Stock, namely, the late roots, and early green crops, should ever be objects of the highest importance to a Farmer who endeavours to keep as much Stock as possible; for Farmers in general admit that they could keep more in other parts of the year, than in the two months preceeding Old-May-Day. This period limits the quantity of Stock kept on every Farm, and also the value of that Stock; for the Farmers profits thereon will be more or less, according to the plentiful or scanty provision for Stock in these two months. Therefore it is evident that the overflowing food of Summer, cannot be consumed to the greatest advantage, without artificially making ample provision for this naturally the greatest ebb-tide of food in all the year.

Another of Smith's manuscripts entitled *Politics, Statistics, &c.* was probably written in 1831 and this extract further reveals the considerable scope of his interests:

That the wealth of a nation depends on the good employment of its inhabitants, cannot be doubted; and if that wealth and employment be equally diffused, its benefits must be general; but if, from any internal natural advantages of the country, wealth, and employment becomes locally and prodigiously increased, and that at the expense of the most valuable article in the country, and if the persons so employed derive their food and the articles they are employed upon from a foreign soil, and if foreign ships be allowed to benefit by the commerce between such privileged locations of trade and foreign market, then the truth of that maxim and its general benefits may be doubted, - And further too, if it can be shown that those acquiring wealth from local advantages in this country applied to a foreign trade, have also superseded the ancient employment of others at home, who have no such natural advantages. That all men have a right to benefit by the natural advantages they possess, must be allowed; it being the principle that all men have acted upon from the earliest locations of population and trade. Most of our ancient cities and boroughs sprung up into consequence from their respective natural advantages in supporting a numerous population, chiefly employed in manufacture and trade, and many of them (whose occupation is gone) were incorporated and enfranchised to encourage and improve those manufactures. It is also well-known that many of the earliest improvements in arts and manufacture, were made by foreigners invited here and incorporated for that purpose, and in one of the Charters of the town of Kidwelly, it is said, that no Welchman shall be of the corporation. This was ever a poor place but many others, originally wealthy and populous, are annually becoming poor, from causes wh. are now powerfully operating against them. It has been said of Salisbury, that no new house has been built therein within a century but upon the site of an old one. This, as well as Exeter, Chichester, Colchester, Ipswich, Norwich and many others, were, in the former state of things, good situations for manufacture and trade, but it being my present object to notice only those locations of Trade wh. depend upon our MINERALS, I shall merely add that Chichester was enriched by the great IRON-TRADE of Sussex, about 100 years since transferred to South Wales. This transfer of wealth, and employment, to the mountains of Wales, where it has been wonderfully extended and improved, arose out of the local advantages of coal, accompanied with iron-stone, in the greatest abundance. From these advantages Iron being cheapened to the lowest degree, the benefits of the transfer are extended all over the Island, and from the raw material being our own, and from the abundant employment the trade affords, no evil whatever can arise from the greatest possible extension of our Iron-trade in Foreign Markets. The transfer of the ALUM TRADE, brought into the country by Sir Thos. Challoner, in the reign of Eliz., and from wh. Whitby and its vicinity derived great wealth and employment, has also been made for the convenience of coal. As new arts arise new articles are required, and thus, to encourage the manufacture of IRON WIRE for cards [wool combs], and in the Woollen manufacture, Germans, in the reign of Eliz., were brought over, and encouraged by a patent to make Iron wire, for that purpose, first at Tintelm in Monmouthshire, and about the same time, two Germans of the name of Wm. Humphrey, & Ch. Sh...tes [as in MS], had the royal privilege of searching the Island for CALAMINE and COPPER, for making Latten [brass]. All the Minerals then belonged to the Crown. The employment afforded by extracting minerals from the mountains in Wales, was prodigious, and the wealth, thence acquired by Sir Hugh Middleton, was all vested in labour to make the new river from Ware to London. It was also from the wealth of those mines that Sir Carberry P..... contested the royal right to minerals, which by an act of Parliament in the reign of Wm. the III., became vested in the owners of the soil. Great wealth and employment arose out of the Copper mines in the Island of Anglesea, for many years. And, I have been told, at the Alshee copper mines on the shores of Bantry Bay, in the south of Ireland, which originated in my suggestions, £5,000 a year was soon paid in labour, and that, in one year, they sent to Swansea 800 tons of copper ore, of the finest quality. These are some of the great advantages of attending to our Minerals as sources of good Employment for the Inhabitants, and consequently of wealth. These benefits from the metallic ores are, however, but local, and in some instances precarious and transferable. The advantages to be derived from the metallic ores, are also known to be confined to certain ranges of strata in the interior, and on the western side of our Island and in those parts confined to certain narrow ranges called veins; but the coarser kinds of minerals, such as all kinds of STONE, SAND, CLAY, &c., wh. are stratified, and applied to many useful purposes are, on account of their now well known regularity and continuity, good sources of employment and profit. No place can be better stored with the articles than the greater part of this Island. They in former times, seem however to have been little attended to, as in the time of Sir Robt. Walpole and probably much later, the streets of the Metropolis were paved with Bremen stone. Purbeck stone was much in use since I can remember, which gave way to the finer flags from Yorks., first introduced by Sir Wm. Stains, and the great employment this kind of stone affords, and

> the profits thereon, between the quarries and their place in the pavement of London and numerous other great Towns, is become a settled national benefit, and to which many new and extended uses of freestone, slate, flints, &c., have largely contributed. All the best kinds of POTTERY called Delft-ware, was formerly imported from Holland, the clay for which, to the disgrace of the country, was taken from our shores, but which, to the immortal memory of Wedgewood [sic], has become a permanent source of employment to many thousands of men, women and children, in the populous but new district of Etruria. This manufacture *to my knowledge* is capable of great extension, and which, like the Iron trade, from the raw materials being our own, is one of the best that the country can encourage for exportation. FLAGS AND GRINDSTONES are the accompaniments of coal, and therefore from their quantity, quality and accessibility, Britain, to the advancement of labour and commerce, might supply all the world with these articles. FLINTS are most extensively used in potteries, which, like the pipe clay, are the chief minerals of value in the south-eastern part of the Island, but to calcine the flints and the ware, these articles go to the coal districts.

Dr. William Hyde Wollaston, after being beaten in a competition for the post of physician to St. George's Hospital in 1800, abandoned medicine and devoted himself to scientific research. He was highly successful, especially in chemistry and optics. He discovered, among many other things, two new metals, palladium and rhodium, the dark lines in the solar spectrum and ultra-violet rays. He invested £1,000 in 3% bonds and directed that, after his death, the Geological Society:

> should apply the dividends in promoting researches concerning the mineral structure of the earth, or in rewarding those by whom such researches should hereafter be made; or in such manner as should appear to the Council of the said Society for the time being, conducive to the interests of the Society in particular, or the science of geology in general.

He went on to instruct the Society:

> not to hoard the dividends parsimoniously, but to expend them liberally, and as far as might be, annually, in furthering the objects of the trust.

With the first year's interest the Society ordered to be made a gold medal bearing the head of Dr. Wollaston. They decided that its first recipient should be William Smith:

> in consideration of his being a great original discoverer in English geology; and especially for his having been the first, in this country, to discover and to teach the identification of strata, and to determine their succession by means of their imbedded fossils.'

The Wollaston Medal of the Geological Society was presented to Smith at their Anniversary Meeting on 18 February 1831, by the then President, Professor Adam Sedgwick, incumbent of the Woodwardian Chair of Geology at Cambridge University and twenty years later a recipient of the Wollaston medal himself. In his address, he said:

> I for one can speak with gratitude of the practical lessons I have received from Mr. Smith. It was by tracking his footsteps, with his maps in my hand, through Wiltshire and the neighbouring counties, where he had trodden nearly thirty years before, that I first learned the subdivisions of our oolitic series, and apprehended the meaning of those arbitrary and somewhat uncouth terms, which we derive from him as our master, which have long become engrafted into the conventional language of English geologists, and through their influence have been, in part, also adopted by the naturalists of the Continent. After such a statement, gentlemen, I have a right to speak boldly, and to demand your approbation of the Council's award. I could almost dare to wish that stern lover of truth, to whose bounty we owe the 'Donation Fund', that dark eye, before the glance of which all false pretensions withered, were once more amongst us. And if it be denied us to hope that a spirit like that of Wollaston should often be embodied on the earth, I would appeal to those intelligent men who form the strength and ornament of this Society, whether there was any place for doubt or hesitation? whether we were not compelled, by every motive which the judgment can approve and the heart can sanction to perform this act of filial duty, before we thought of the claims of any other man, and to place our first honour on the brow of the father of English geology?
>
> If, in the pride of our present strength, we were disposed to forget our origin, our very speech would bewray us; for we use the language which he taught us in the infancy of our science. If we, by our united efforts, are chiselling the ornaments and slowly raising up the pinnacles of one of the temples of nature, it was he who gave the plan, and laid the foundations, and erected a portion of the solid walls by the unassisted labour of his hands.
>
> The men who have led the way in useful discoveries have ever held the first place of honour in the estimation of all who in aftertimes have understood their works or trodden in their steps. It is upon this abiding

> principle that we have acted: and in awarding our first prize to Mr. Smith, we believe that we have done honour to our own body, and are sanctioned by the highest feelings which bind societies together.
>
> I think it a high privilege to fill this chair on an occasion when we are met: not coldly to deliberate on the balance of conflicting claims, in which, after all, we might go wrong, and give the prize to one man by injustice to another; but to perform a sacred duty, where there is no room for doubt or error, and to perform an act of public gratitude, in which the judgment and the feelings are united.'

The medal itself was not made in time for the presentation and it was not actually given to Smith until the occasion of the second meeting of the British Association (founded in York in 1831) at Oxford in June, 1832. There was a tiny flaw in the die, which was later removed, so Smith's medal is slightly imperfect. It is therefore possible positively to identify the actual one which he received, the first to be awarded. At this meeting, he also received the news that the Government had been persuaded by representatives of British science to grant him a pension of £100 a year.

After receiving the honour, Smith presented to the Geological Society the original *Table of Stratification*, which he had drawn up in 1799. He also gave them his circular map of the vicinity of Bath, which had been geologically coloured at about the same time, and the first draft of his *General Map of the Strata found in England and Wales* (1801). It is evident from omissions and errors that this last was indeed drawn up in 1801, and that no later additions were made to it. The gifts were doubtless to ensure that Smith's claims to the priority of his discoveries were not disputed in the future. He was seeking to perpetuate his name after his death. These documents were critically examined by Professor J.W. Judd in or just before 1897, and photographs of them placed in the Science Museum, South Kensington, the library of the Geological Society, and the Natural History and British Museums.

At the Geological Society's second meeting in Oxford in 1832, Smith distributed a *Synopsis of Geological Phenomena*. This gives an interesting insight into the state of scientific knowledge at that time. It included statements such as:

> shells in rocks not crushed – therefore rocks hardened quickly; the trade winds and sea currents are existing effects of the earth's centrifugal force; by the spheroidal figure of the earth – water as well as land is 13 miles higher under the equator than at the poles; by the bouldered stones every where scattered over the earth's surface – there has been water in action; by the height to which the boulders and sea-shells have been raised – we get the force of action and height of the water – THE DELUGE.

The *Synopsis* also features 'Illustrative Effects of the Deluge'. Smith cites:

> by alum shale, organised fossils, those of coal, and mountain limestone, and boulders from all the rocks northward, in abundance – the effects of a great current from the N. are obvious on the Yorkshire coast – the first rush of water was by sea from the North; by sea shells under 20 feet of gravel – 1000 feet high in Snowdon mountains – with wonderful uplaying from N.W.; by bouldered chalk and flints, far in – Northamptonshire, Rutland and Huntingdon – currents from S. and S.E..

These are just a few of the phenomena Smith mentions.

Smith spent nearly all his time quietly at Hackness, but was rejuvenated when the time came for meetings of the British Association. He did not, however, join in discussions, only speaking when he had something striking to say. This may to some extent have been the consequence of the only burden he had to bear as a result of old age, a slight deafness, and he was disappointed to miss some of the wit and eloquence of Adam Sedgwick.

Following a meeting of the British Association in Edinburgh in 1834, he visited Sir Charles Monteith, and took the opportunity of studying the geology of Closeburn and Nithsdale, to the north-west of Dumfries. Here he found and brought home specimens of the coral-rich Silurian sandstone, similar to those well known in Shropshire and South Wales.

That same year Smith felt the desire to leave his employment at Hackness and return to Scarborough. Five years later, in a note datelined Scarborough, 28 June, 1839, he wrote:

> After living at Hackness near six years I grew weary of nothing but farming concerns, and told my good friend Sir John Johnstone I wished to leave it, and that as the last five or six years of a man's life were seldom good for much, I wished to have them to myself (provided I lived so long), to complete and arrange my papers without the interruption of any business, to which he readily acceded, and kindly allowed me twenty pounds a year for occasional advice and visits.

Rather than arranging his papers, Smith steadily added to them. It later became clear from the datelines, that he had also been very active in writing at Hackness, which showed that he had not been entirely engrossed in farming matters. He spent the next few years happily at Scarborough in his study surrounded by his maps and papers, or strolling under the cliffs, whose geological structure he had been the first to understand.

He made occasional visits to London, but his increasing deafness deprived him of much of the pleasure such trips should have brought. He travelled to Dublin with the British Association in 1835, and there totally unexpectedly received an honorary Doctorate of Laws (LL.D.) from Trinity College. Whilst on that side of the Irish Sea, he was taken by the Dean of Trinity College, the Rev. J. Maclean, to many interesting places in the north of Ireland. He met the Director of Operations of the Geological Survey in Ireland, Captain Portlock, and discussed with him matters of great import to the countryside there, drainage and the improvement of agricultural land.

In 1836, the people of Bristol asked Dr. Smith to attend a meeting there of the British Association. He was delighted to meet old friends and to revisit sites he had not seen for thirty years. He carried out a meticulous study of the coal district of Kingswood and coloured in the results of his observation on sheets of the Ordnance Survey.

The first volume of *The Magazine of Natural History* New Series, 1837 (usually known as *Charlesworth's Magazine)*, contained two articles by Dr. Smith. The first was entitled *Practical Distinctions in Minerals*:

> On March 31st, 1836, I discovered that the finest particles of mica and quartz in stone may be readily distinguished without the aid of glasses; and, conceiving that this simple method of knowing the difference in some of our most common minerals may be serviceable to geologists, I beg the insertion of it in your most useful magazine.
>
> With this view, therefore, without attempting any philosophical explanation of the phenomenon, I merely relate the circumstances of its practical application: first observing, with pleasure, that the eye, which gives us the power of knowing so much, and of knowing one thing from another so distinctly, without our being able to explain how we make the distinctions, is happily receiving from Sir David Brewster, [who discovered how to calculate the refractive index of a glass surface], and other philosophers in optical science, that attention it is entitled to.
>
> My sight has been particularly good, having been able to distinguish objects very clearly, near and at a great distance; and now, in my 69th year, I can distinguish a small speck of mica, in a brown-red sandstone, at the distance of 4 yards; and, *in the full bright light of the sun* the brilliant reflections from facets of much smaller crystals of quartz. I was led to this experiment by finding amongst our Scarborough gravel, a brown red sandstone pebble the crystal of which brilliantly reflected the full light of the sun. Viewing it in the house, on a table before my window, with my spectacles on, and the addition of a small pocket lens, the glistening specks appeared too small for me to decide whether they consisted of quartz or mica; but, as I had lately selected from the same gravel specimens of mica slate, and mica sandstones of all degrees of fineness, it occurred to

> me that small specks of mica were always visible without the sun's full bright light. I found them so; and by collating the sandstone with the finest grained micaceous specimen, both on one piece of paper shifted alternately into the bright and shady light of the sun, we have a clear and ready distinction, between the finest grains of mica and quartz, without the aid of glasses, and that even at a distance of 4 yards.
>
> In my practical observations on the different kinds of land, I had long observed, by the glistening in footpaths, how we may readily distinguish the finest sand in soil; and, at Harrogate, I have often amused myself, on the nicely sanded footpaths about the Swan Hotel, by fixing my eye upon any detached crystal (of mill-stone grit) which brilliantly reflected the light of the sun, and not without speculating on the application of such brilliant reflections to some useful purpose; but in geology, the brilliancy of those facets of quartz crystals in our coarsest sandstone seems to render doubtful the 'theory of sandstones being derivative rocks'.
>
> William Smith, LL.D.,
> Scarborough, May 10th, 1837.

In 1838, Dr. Smith was appointed by the government to be a member of a small commission to select the building stone for the new Palace of Westminster. On this he served with Sir Charles Barry, one of the architects of the building, and Henry Thomas De La Beche (later knighted), head of the Geological Survey and founder of the Museum of Economic Geology and the School of Mines. After a meeting of the British Association in Newcastle, they spent August, September and October travelling rapidly across a large part of England and Wales. They collected a wealth of information on the sites of over a hundred quarries, the cost and 'workability' of the stones and their record of durability in older buildings. Their report was published on 16 March 1839 and the stone selected was the firm, yellow, granular magnesian limestone of Bolsover Moor in Derbyshire. Dr. Smith's contribution to the commission had been most valuable.

A manuscript memorandum in connection with this work was published after his death:

FREESTONE

> The Hackness Stone is a fine-grained silicious Freestone chiefly of a mellow brownish yellow colour, or what is commonly called a good stone colour. Rubbed and finely jointed this stone presents a smooth surface and a most agreeable appearance in passages, halls, etc., and externally in fronts of Houses Churches and other public buildings is unequalled in colour and beauty of ornamental work. Hackness Hall

built of this stone thirty years since [1805] is a proof of its good qualities. The stone being naturally dry and unabsorbent of moisture neither suffers by damp from the earth or by exposure to sun rain or frost nor does it moulder in sheltered places under cornices, like many other of the soft freestones.

It is not essentially necessary that this stone should be placed in its bed – stones for columns 12 or 15 feet or more in length may be raised from beds 2 to 5 feet in thickness. When raised from the quarry this stone is soft but hardens by exposure, works free and tough with any kind of tools receives and preserves the finest arriss of any stone in use may be turned and carved into the finest kind of ornamental work required, which by specimens thereof in Hackness Hall appear likely ever to retain their form and sharpness.

BUILDING STONE

A hard compact silicious stone even in texture and free from extraneous matter, of little but uniform colour, brownish white – neither splits scales or moulders by the longest exposure – capable of being wrought with a pick, point, or chisel, rubs down to a good surface for steps and other purposes; and though hard this stone requires but little working from the great facility of cleaving it either in or across the bed. 'Four or five feet of the upper part of the rock is sufficiently lamellar to cleave for Flags which require but little dressing – may be firmly jointed and are very strong and durable, and placed edgewise for Curbstones are not liable to split. The blocks may be easily cleft for area or cellar steps sills or Linterns and may be placed endways for pillars or large Columns. The Stone may be raised from the quarry, from beds 2 feet and upwards in thickness or any portable length and width and from its firmness this stone will suffer less damage from carriage than any in the London market. For Bridges Docks Wharf Walls and all kind of heavy works on the Thames, & for Piers and Harbours this stone is particularly well calculated as by the longest exposure to air and salt water it suffers no change. This stone is excellent for sound and strong Troughs or Cisterns.

Smith was in good health and spirits, when he returned to Scarborough. In early July he initiated arrangements for the tenure of his comfortable house in Huntriss Row (now demolished) for several more years. He left it on the 5th of the month, never to return.

On 10 July, he attended a meeting of the English Agricultural Society in Cavendish Square, London, and went on to Oxford on 16th to dine with 2,500 people at Queen's College. Afterwards he spent some time in the countryside to the south of the city, revisited Churchill for a few days, and then returned to London on 9 August.

Dr. Smith was especially invited to attend a meeting of the British Association in Birmingham on 26th. En route, he stayed at the house of highly-valued friends, George Baker, a magistrate of Northampton, archaeologist and medievalist, and his sister, Miss Ann Elizabeth Baker. He made several excursions into the neighbouring countryside. He contracted what he thought of as a slight cold, of which he made light, though it was probably influenza. He suffered from diarrhoea and his condition deteriorated seriously within the next few days. With his nephew at his bedside, he died at 10pm on 28 August,1839. He is buried under a large, but unmarked gravestone, a few feet from the west tower of the lovely old church of St. Peter, Marefair, Northampton. A memorial tablet and bust, funded by subscriptions from fellow geologists, were placed against the west wall of the nave, south of the grand Norman arch over the entrance to the tower. The pedestal on which the rough white unpolished marble bust is mounted is inscribed:

TO HONOUR THE NAME OF
WILLIAM SMITH, LL.D.
THIS MONUMENT IS ERECTED BY HIS FRIENDS
AND FELLOW LABOURERS IN THE FIELD OF
BRITISH GEOLOGY.
BORN 23rd MARCH 1769 AT CHURCHILL IN OXFORDSHIRE,
AND TRAINED TO THE PROFESSION OF A CIVIL ENGINEER AND
MINERAL SURVEYOR, HE BEGAN IN 1791 TO SURVEY
COLLIERIES AND PLAN CANALS IN THE VICINITY OF BATH,
AND, HAVING OBSERVED THAT THE SEVERAL STRATA OF THAT
DISTRICT WERE CHARACTERIZED BY PECULIAR GROUPS OF
ORGANIC REMAINS HE ADOPTED THIS FACT AS A PRINCIPLE
OF COMPARISON AND WAS BY IT ENABLED TO IDENTIFY
THE STRATA IN DISTANT PARTS OF THIS ISLAND
TO CONSTRUCT SECTIONS AND TO COMPLETE AND PUBLISH
IN 1815 A GEOLOGICAL MAP OF ENGLAND AND WALES.
BY THUS DEVOTING, DURING HIS WHOLE LIFE, ALL THE POWER
OF AN OBSERVING MIND TO THE ADVANCEMENT OF ONE
BRANCH OF SCIENCE, HE GAINED THE TITLE OF THE
'FATHER OF ENGLISH GEOLOGY.'
WHILE ON HIS WAY TO A MEETING OF THE BRITISH ASSOCIATION
FOR THE ADVANCEMENT OF SCIENCE, AT BIRMINGHAM,
HE DIED IN THIS TOWN, AT THE HOUSE OF HIS FRIEND
GEORGE BAKER, THE HISTORIAN OF NORTHAMPTONSHIRE.
28th OF AUGUST 1839.

33. St. Peter's, Marefair, Northampton, in which a memorial tablet and bust to William Smith are mounted.

The bust is a replica of the original made in 1848 by Matthew Noble, an eminent sculptor and native of Hackness. There are also copies in the British Museum of Natural History, and at the Geological Society of London.

Eleven weeks after Smith's death, Sir John Johnstone wrote to Philip Pusey, M.P. a note entitled *On the Application of Geology to Agriculture.* He said:

> In compliance with your request that I would furnish you with the particulars of the geological map and survey of my Yorkshire estate, made several years ago by Dr. Smith (whose recent loss we have to deplore), with the view of enabling you to ascertain how far the facts and practical results thus obtained are likely to elucidate the necessary connexion between geology and agriculture, I have much pleasure in placing the following observations in your hands, begging you will make any use you please of them in illustrating an inquiry of so useful and interesting a nature.
>
> In the year 1828, having observed great variations in the soils upon my estate, not only on the sides of the hills, which might be expected, but also in the fields upon the table-land forming the summits of these hills, and which, from being flat, or rather declining to the south with a gradual and easy slope, rendered the variation more difficult to explain, I mentioned the subject to Dr. Smith, who was then lecturing at Scarborough, and surveying the surrounding district, with the view of

34. Bust of Smith in St. Peter's, Northampton.

proving the identity of the Hackness strata with those near Oxford. He at once offered a solution of my difficulty, by a reference to geology; and, having gone over minutely the fields in question, with a reduced map of my estate in his hands, he marked upon it, in different colours, the ranges of these strata, as they exhibited themselves into zones or breadths of one, two, or more fields together, according as the particular stratum which came to the surface was more or less horizontal, or more or less thick.

The result thus obtained clearly demonstrated that the value of each field, and the mode of cultivation already adopted (with the exception of the use of lime, which had been too frequently and too indiscriminately applied to the entire estate), corresponded to the variations of the strata, and were limited by the areas which these occupied on the surface: thus showing that (though the results had been

35. Smith's grave, St. Peter's, Northampton.

arrived at by the farmers through a different process, viz., trial and error) the geological character of a country, when accurately understood, pointed out at once the natural value of the land, and the system of cultivation best adapted to it. For instance, on the highest range of my hills, a few fields, without any apparent reason, have been universally productive in all seasons, more so than the fields adjoining them on a lower level, and which appear *nearly* of the same quality. The fossils, and other marks well understood by Dr. Smith, proved them to consist of an insulated portion of the UPPER calcareous grit formation, which also produces an excellent tract of land in another part of Yorkshire.

So also through all the successive divisions of the upper oolitic series, which compose this estate, it was seen that the best upland grass-land was on the peculiar zone or stratum formed on the coralline oolite through all the farms, though separated from each other by wide intervals.

We also discovered what, when followed out in other districts, may prove a most valuable fact, that the wheat is usually only thrown out in severe frosts upon those fields formed by this same coralline oolite; the same cause having no effect upon the *adjoining fields*, which are on a different stratum, lower in the series, and of a sandy nature, with no calcareous matter in them.

Sir John goes on to say:

> When, on descending the hill-sides, it was found that there were certain fields which, whether towards the south or north, whatever the aspect, whatever the local circumstances (so long as not too steep to be ploughed), invariably produced good wheat, it was a triumph for agricultural geology to discover that these fields were invariably upon the Oxford clay, or rather where the lower beds of the calc. Grit become mixed up with that formation.

Later, he adds:

> My geological map at once points out all those portions of the estate which consist of this stratum [the coralline oolite beds], and upon which there is obviously no necessity for lime; and I am thus saved from the task which otherwise I should have to encounter of analysing the soil of each individual field.....Certain soils are so obviously connected with their bases, that we need scarcely ask how geology and agriculture are linked together; and to use Dr. Smith's own words, 'The strata succeed each other in a certain order, and, being delineated a knowledge of the strata becomes the natural and safe foundation of improvement; and if agricultural chemistry be ever successfully applied to the practical purposes of agriculture, it must be by proceeding with the chemical analysis of soils along the range of each stratum.'

In 1869, W. Stephen Mitchell contributed some notes on *The Centenary of William Smith's Birth* to the *Geological Magazine*. He concluded his article:

> The connection of William Smith with Bath during the development of his geological ideas, is thus summarised: - The examination of the district between High Littleton and Bath first led him to suppose a regularity in the succession of all the strata; the planning of the Somersetshire Coal Canal near Bath, was the cause of the tour through England which enabled him to confirm his supposition: the difficulty in distinguishing 'the oolitic rocks on and near the end of the canal towards Bath led him to the discovery of a mode of *identifying* the strata by the organized fossils respectively embedded therein.
>
> The *first* collection of fossils stratigraphically arranged was made by him at Cottage Crescent, Bath.
>
> The *first* table of the order of strata was drawn up by him at Pulteney Street, Bath.
>
> The *first* geological map known is his map of the district of Bath [but Jean Etienne Guettard had published two in France in 1752].

> The *first* geological map of England was coloured by him while living near Bath.
>
> The *first* announcement of the publication of a geological map of England, was his 'prospectus' dated from Midford, Bath.
>
> The *first* introduction of his discovery to public notice, was through the friends he made in Bath.

Except when he was receiving his education, John Phillips lived and worked with his uncle from the age of eight. He began to make his own career in geology after he was twenty-one, but still supported his uncle in many projects, right up to Smith's death eighteen years later. His summary of his life and character is therefore written from intimate knowledge:

> Dr. Smith's person was formed on large proportions, corresponding to the sturdy strength of his intellect; his health was generally good; he enjoyed a sound mind in a sound body. When about forty years of age he suffered by ague [malaria], caught in the marshes of Laugharn, and at subsequent times by diarrhoea, probably through exposure to cold, which he always faced without a great-coat, or the defence of hand-shoes, as he contemptuously termed gloves. To slight attacks of lumbago he was rather subject, and from about the fiftieth to the sixtieth year he was troubled by a gravel complaint; this was relieved by copious drafts of vegetable bitters (camomile tea), and by this treatment and extreme moderation in diet, followed by abstinence for a time from all fermented liquors, entirely cured, so that in the latter years of his life he was apparently and really free from illness. Descended from a healthy race, amongst whom tooth-ache was unknown and longevity was frequent - uncles and great-grandfathers having seen their 98th year - temperate in diet; moderate in exercise, and vigorous in mind, his whole life was a continuous stream of thought and action. He can hardly be said or supposed to have lost by neglect a single hour, though, by permitting his mind to wander from its appointed line of research into innumerable by-paths, he sometimes forgot or postponed, and therefore failed in his main object.
>
> A remarkable quality in the character of Smith was firmness, which, according to the difficulties, disappointments and sorrows of his life, took the aspect of fortitude, patience and resignation; but in the prosecution of scientific or professional labour, rose to cheerful courage and persevering resolution. The exercise of this high quality gained him in early life professional independence and scientific fame, and in later years preserved to him, amidst

poverty and domestic affliction, a calm elastic mind, the envy of younger men.

The 'Map of the Strata of England and Wales' is a monument of labour and judgment: if to this we add twenty-one geological maps of counties and many detailed sections, a great variety of reports in engineering and mineral surveying, and innumerable detached essays on geological and economical subjects, we shall grant to the author and writer the praise of unremitting industry. More abundant fruits of this industry would have been given to the world had he been more regularly trained, especially in literary pursuits; for thus the excessive aptitude of his mind for original and discursive research might have been directed in more methodical channels to more systematic and complete results.

The life of a professional man, and especially that of an engineer, is seldom favourable for the acquirement of the valuable habit of restricted and regular study: Smith's career was in all respects such as to render the exercise of this habit impracticable; his papers have been mostly written at short intervals of rest while travelling, and are thus only fragments which the author alone could have arranged into an edifice - links of a broken chain which can never be re-united.

Voluminous as these papers are, they do not contain a vast variety of matters which had passed under Smith's observation. His memory retained whatever his eyes had seen; and it has often occurred to friends who listened to his precise and complete narrations of past events, to regret that no practised amanuensis was at hand to preserve much that ought not to have been lost. There are living geologists who may be warned by these remarks how to provide against the mischiefs of indolence or indisposition, and by the humble aid of swift writing, to save for future times those precious thoughts which else will exist only in the fading recollections of admiring friends.

Had Smith been asked what he thought the most prevailing quality of his mind, he would doubtless have replied 'a habit of observation'.

In a note written in Scarborough, dated November 16, 1838, he says:

By these reminiscences I see how the habit of observation crept on me, gained a settlement in my mind, became a constant associate of my life, and started up in activity at the first thoughts of a journey; so that I generally went off well prepared with maps, and sometimes with contemplations on its objects, or on those on the road, reduced to writing, before it commenced. My mind was therefore like the canvas of a painter, well prepared for the first and best impressions.

Phillips goes on with his summary:

> This habit, founded on natural quickness of the senses, was nourished in boyhood and cultivated through life. The eye was in him more than in other men the avenue of knowledge to the mind, and was educated with proportionate care. Often, when desirous of remembering a certain name, he would write it distinctly, saying, that if he forgot the sound he should remember the picture. This memory for form made him an easy and accurate sketcher, and, with a good taste for colour, gave him great enjoyment in paintings and sculptures.
>
> The colouring of the great Map of the Strata was on a new and peculiar plan, the terminal edges of the rocks being deeply tinted and the other parts of their visible surface merely washed; the constructing and colouring of the sections were equally unlike what were adopted previously; the very shelves on which his primitive collection was arranged bore the same impress of original and independent thought. These were in wood what the sections were on paper, the boards being made all to slope in one direction, so as to imitate the prevalent inclination of the rocks: and their terminal edges rising to greater or less heights above the floor, according as the rocks which they represented formed hills or valleys on the earth's surface. This arrangement has been partially copied in the beautiful Rotunda at Scarborough [nicknamed the Pepperpot], in the plan and execution of which on many points Smith's advice was followed.
>
> A man whose life was passed in reducing to order the rugged aspect of the earth, might claim to be excused for any slight want of refinement in manner; but Dr. Smith's natural goodness of heart and variety of knowledge rendered his society agreeable to most persons, and highly attractive to those who valued him or the science he had unfolded. In his intercourse with such friends the '*malus pudor*' [a poor sense of honour] and the '*superbia quaesita meritis*' [exaggerated arrogance], which seem to haunt men of genius, were driven away by an unrestrained flow of pleasant narration, or an earnest pleading for what was deemed true, and sacred because true. On such occasions, the resolution with which he held to an opinion once formed on one good, or on several plausible reasons, might deviate into prejudice, if the arguments brought to oppose him were not of such a nature as he deemed fitting for the case. He would yield always to a plain and clear statement of fact, but seldom to a demonstration involving or founded on the progress of collateral science. Geology was with him 'the science,' with its own classes of observations, arguments and conclusions. Such light as zoology, botany, chemistry, or mechanics could throw on the ancient phaenomena of

nature was admitted slowly and cautiously, unless independently sustained by direct observations on the strata; and as for their verification he would seldom trust others than himself, his views of geological theory were sometimes difficult and embarrassed.

A favourite topic of conversation with Dr. Smith was the history of his own geological researches, coupled with notices of his professional labours, and doubtless there are many persons now living who have heard from his lips a more full and circumstantial account of several events of his life than it was necessary or indeed practicable to record in these pages. They will also remember innumerable pleasant anecdotes and characteristic traits of many eminent individuals with whom he had been associated. It is difficult to resist the temptation of reporting these amusing notices of events which happened half a century since but a very small selection must suffice.

On occasion of a visit to Mr. Crawshay at Merthyr Tydvil (1803), he had an opportunity of hearing the sentiments of a brother ironmaster on the subject of teaching the art of writing to poor children, then debated in the midst of the furnaces. 'No, no,' exclaimed this really intelligent and benevolent, if prejudiced man, 'they'll all be hanged for forgery; put 'em into a three-foot vein,' - a thickness of coal esteemed to be suitable for 'training up a child in the way he should go!'

Being consulted by a landowner on the dry Mendip Hills, as to the best means of procuring supplies of water for his farm, Smith found that he had been anticipated in delivering an opinion on this very difficult subject by a miner, who proposed to solve the problem by divination, that is to say, by the divining or jowsing (chowsing?) rod. Unwilling that his worthy employer should be at the mercy of this superstition, he filled his pockets with some small stones not commonly found on the Mendips, and proceeded to witness the trial of the 'forked stick'. Accordingly the miner exercised, in presence of the owner and the geologist, the 'mystery' of the rod, and wherever the point of the twig turned downward, declared that water was to be found by digging. At these points Smith quietly dropped the stones, and when several places had been thus pitched upon, asked the miner if he could rediscover the points indicated. Unaware of the stratagem, the man readily agreed to repeat the trials on the way home. In his progress he unluckily passed the spots where the stones lay and stopped at several other localities, to which the faithless rod directed attention; on which Smith remarked, that as the water had in so short a time changed its situation at all the points, it would be imprudent to spend money in following it.

On reviewing the course of William Smith's life and labours, we have been forcibly struck with the adaptation of his character to his position, and impressed with the difficulty of judging of a man's mental powers by his practical deeds, - of a man's real enjoyment of life by the merely external circumstances which surround him. Who that heard the hearty laugh of the 'narrative old man', would suppose that he had lost 'house and land', spent more than the hard earnings of his daily life and endured of what is called affliction more than commonly falls to the lot of man? Who that knew what he had endured, could believe that, in the heaviest hour, he had never yielded to depression, never ceased to command his mind and turn its unfailing energy to the subjects he *willed* to contemplate? Any one, aware of the disadvantages from which he rose into renown. might suppose his great discoveries to have been the sudden result of accident, rather than the growth of exact observation and careful reflection. Yet in all these cases the first impressions would be utterly in error. Perhaps a greater error than all would be the supposition that, under more flourishing worldly circumstances, the labours of this remarkable man would have been greatly more important.
He did not think so himself. They who argue thus are perhaps not right in their general view of human nature, and certainly they are wrong in the estimate they form of the character of Smith. Heads which brave the attacks of adversity, yield to the solicitation of prosperity. There was in the luxurious musing which he indulged somewhat of indolence, and it required often the pressure of business and the lack of money to rouse him to needful exertion. Except by the peculiar profession which he created for himself, the peculiar work which he set himself to do, the gathering of materials for his great Map, could not have been accomplished by an individual.

It has been conjectured that the progress of English geology would have been accelerated had the infant Geological Society of 1808 taken up Smith's principles, and adopted his map as a basis of operations. *It is very improbable that he would have agreed to share with any man, or any body of men, the labour and the honour of the work,* on which he felt himself entitled to write, 'Alone I did it.' Whether he was right in the opinion he formed of the value and independence of his researches, and of his own power to follow them out, is not now to be questioned; it may be, however, worth while, before closing this record, to attempt to mark with precision the place in the scale of geological discovery which has been awarded to William Smith by the unanimous vote of contemporary geologists.

Very many *facts* are known by experience before the laws which unite these facts into system are embodied into science. The stratification of many rocks; the alternation of rocks of different nature; the peculiar positions of metallic veins; these and many other circumstances, which are now known in the shape of general *laws of phaenomena*, must have been known in the mines and collieries and quarries of Europe from an early period of the middle ages. The quality and distribution of soils: the characteristic features of ranges of hills; the peculiarities of the origin and course of many rivers: these and other facts observable on the *surface of the earth*, which are now seen to depend on the peculiar qualities and positions of rocks below the surface, were formally known as insulated facts, and, in some instances, may have suggested to such men as Packe, and Lister, and Evelyn, views of the earth's structure more conformable to modern philosophy than appear in their writings.

The glimpses of general truth which those early writers obtained constitute a considerable body of knowledge, and are far more worthy of a place in the history of English geology than the sounding speculations of Burnet, and Whiston, and even Whitehurst, great as are the merits in other respects of that remarkable author.

In *New Light on William Smith and his Work*, L.R. Cox says:

Of his appearance in middle age, perhaps the most active period of his crowded life, fewer records, however, remain.

'Strata Smith,' as he was then universally called, was doubtless a familiar character in many provincial towns and in the various inns along the coach routes by which he made his incessant journeys, accompanied by bundles of maps and papers. One pictures him, in his thirties and forties, as a hale and hearty, well-built man, somewhat bluff in manner and broad of accent, restless and full of energy; ready to converse, with friend or stranger upon many subjects, but usually reverting finally to his favourite topic – the strata of the earth and the application of their study to agriculture, mining and all works of public utility.

As yet he had far to go before he was to achieve fame, and those references to him which I have been able to trace in the literature of the period are mostly brief.. To what extent he was possessed of the gift of seeing himself as others saw him it is difficult to say. An account of his appearance in middle age, written by himself much later in life, deserves, however, to be quoted. After remarking that he had never been assaulted or insulted in his life, although his professional work had taken him much among miners, 'navigators' [the 'navvies', who dug the canals], and men of a similar type, he goes on to remark:

I have often thought my strong, muscular appearance, firm step, steady, straightforward, 'quick-eyed,' and perhaps rather stern look contributed much to my safety; for I once heard some men behind me in London (whose manners I did not much like) say, one to the other, 'He's a d……d good built one.' I have been asked whether I had never been a pugilist. Some strangers have said, 'I suspect, Sir, you have been a great walker in your time'; and strangers, also met with in my travels, have suspected that I had been a soldier.

I have often been taken for a Scotsman perhaps for my robust make and some trace of the broad Oxfordshire dialect; but many travellers with whom I have conversed have said that, in this respect, they could form no idea of what part of the country I came from: and others, seeing my eye and sometimes my pencil actively employed on the road, could not conceive what could be my occupation, but, if there seemed a chance of their knowing anything about the country, I, like Dr. Franklin, soon let them know what I was.

In great towns, dissenters would eye me across the street, as if they thought I belonged to them; and particularly the Quakers, perhaps from a resemblance in habiliment and a rather broad hat.

Portraits, Busts and Memorials

Following the Holkham sheep-shearing in 1805, some of the eminent people who had attended gathered at Smith's house in Buckingham Street, London, where they sat for a group portrait by Solomon Williams. William Smith was included, behind Sir Joseph Banks. This picture was never finished. It was said to be in Smith's possession in 1839, but has not to date been discovered. Williams did later complete an oil painting of Smith, but it was thought not to be a very good likeness. Smith was talented at drawing and sketched a small profile portrait of himself (probably with the aid of mirrors) in February, 1808. Sadly it is now disfigured by mildew. However, his slightly receding forehead, firm mouth, rather large nose and mutton-chop side-whiskers seen in later life are recognisable.

In 1832, Smith's friends in Scarborough gave him a letter of introduction to a celebrated artist, John Jackson, who produced a pencil stippling portrait, but sadly he fell ill and died shortly afterwards. The drawing was sold as part of his effects. It is therefore fortunate that a young French artist, Hugues Fourau, who was lodging in the same house as Smith in the summer of 1837, turned out a very fine portrait of him aged 69, otherwise we would have little recording his likeness. It is featured on the front cover of this book. For many years the work hung behind the President's Chair in the Meeting Room of the Geological Society of London in Burlington House, but following refurbishment of the building was recently moved to the eastern staircase. In the frame beneath it is preserved a lock of Smith's hair. Also at the bottom of the same stairs is one of the original copies of his great geological map of 1815. Only by

36. Memorial to Smith at his birthplace in Churchill, Oxfordshire.

seeing its size can one appreciate what an incredible achievement it was. In the corner is a plaster copy of Matthew Noble's bust of Smith, made posthumously in 1848. The one in St. Peter's Church, Northampton, is of marble, as is another at Oxford; a plaster copy is in the British Museum of Natural History in South Kensington.

The Geological Society displays four of Smith's county maps on its walls and other maps and sections, including the one entitled *London towards Snowdon*, are available in the library for genuine researchers and Members. In 1977, the Geological Society instituted the William Smith Medal for Applied Geology.

A bust in the Rotunda Museum was taken from life by a personal friend, Joseph Brogden Baker of Scarborough, probably a relative of George. Copies of this are also in Hackness Hall and with the York Philosophical Society. Casts of his head were made in 1837 by Deville in London and by Butler in Scarborough. Neither of these last two has survived. The bust and memorial tablet in St. Peter's, Northampton, are described on page 134.

A plaque commemorating the dictation in 1799 of Smith's tabular list of strata at 29 Great Pulteney Street, Bath, was unveiled on the house in 1926 by Dr. F.A. Bather.

A fifteen-foot-high monument to Smith was erected in Churchill by Lord Ducie in 1891. It is constructed of large blocks of local oolitic limestone, appropriately enough, since it was Smith who gave the name Oolite to this rock, which forms the higher ground of the area surrounding the village of his birth.

References

Briggs, A., (1983) *A Social History of England*. London.

Cox, L.R. (1940) (Lecture on the Life and Work of William Smith, 1769-1839). Abstr. Proc. Geol. Soc., 1939-40, 23-27.

Cox, L.R. *New Light on William Smith and his Work*. Proc. Yorks. Geol. Soc., 25.

Crawford, W. (1896) *Reminiscences of a Yorkshire Naturalist*.

Debenham, L.S. (1972) *Scarborough's Water Supply*. Transactions of the Scarborough and District Archaeological Society, 2, No. 15.

Dictionary of Earth Sciences, Concise Oxford, 1991. Oxford.

Dictionary of Scientific Biography, 1975: 12, 486-92.

Douglas, J.A. and Cox, L.R., (1949). *Geology Magazine*, 86.

Eyles, J.M. (1974) *William Smith's Home near Bath: the real Tucking Mill*. J. Soc. Biblphy. nat. Hist. 7(1): 29-34.

Eyles, J.M. (1984) *William Smith and the United States*. Earth Science History, 3, 54-57.

Eyles, V.A. & J.M. (1938) *On the different issues of the first geological map of England and Wales*. Annals of Science, 3.

Fenton, C.L. & M.A., (1952). *Giants of Geology*, 29.

Fitton, W.H., (1818) *Edinburgh Review*. Notes on the progress of English geology.

Flett, J.S. (1939) *Pioneers of British Geology*.

Hemingway, J.E. and Owen, J.S. (1974) *William Smith and the Jurassic Coals of Yorkshire*. Proc. Yorks. Geol. Soc.,40, part 3, No. 18, 297-308, pls. 20-22, 14 March, 1975.

Johnstone, J.V.B. (1839) *On the Application of Geology to Agriculture*. Journ. Roy. Agric. Soc., I, 271-5.

Judd, J.W. (1897) *Geology Magazine*, 439-447.

Knell, S.J. (2000) *The Culture of English Geology*, 1815-1851.

Osborne, R. (1998) *The Floating Egg*.

Phillips, J. (1844) *Memoirs of William Smith, LL.D*. London.

Sheppard, T. (1917) (1920 reprint). *William Smith: His Maps and Memoirs*. Hull.

Smith, W. (1805) Account of the improvement of Prisley Bog. Trans. Soc. Arts, 23, 148-172.

Warner, R.N. (1830). *Literary Recollections*.

Wilford, J.N. (1985) *The Riddle of the Dinosaur*.

Appendix 1

Fossil species first named by William Smith in his *Strata identified by Organized Fossils*

Cirrus depressus. 'Lower Chalk', Warminster, Wiltshire. This has a higher spire than the specimen similarly named by Mantel in 1822, but is the same as his *C. perspectivus*.

Inoceramus cuvieri. Smith gave the horizon for this as 'Lower Chalk' from Heytesbury, Wiltshire. However, it is not the species of that name in Sowerby's *Mineral Conchology*, but is *I. involutus*, an Upper Chalk fossil. Examination of the adhering matrix seems to indicate it comes from Upper Chalk. Smith's record of its origin may therefore well have been wrong.

Madrepora porpites. 'Upper Oolite', Broadfield Farm.

Ostrea delta. 'Oak-Tree (Kimmeridge) Clay'. This name first appeared on the back page of the blue cover of Sowerby's *Mineral Conchology*, but as it is referred to in the text of the book as *0. deltoidea* this may have been a misprint.

Terebratulata digona. 'Cornbrash'.

Terebratula pectinata. 'Green Sand'.

These names were introduced by Smith in (to give the publication its full name) *Stratigraphical System of Organized Fossils with reference to the Specimens of the Original Geological Collection in the British Museum: explaining their State of Preservation and their Use in identifying the British Strata*:

Ammonites calix. 'Under Oolite', Sherborn, (now) Avon.

Ammonites modiolaris. 'Fuller's Earth Rock'. Dundry, (now) Avon and Lansdown, Gloucestershire.

Ammonites radiatus. 'Inferior Oolite, between Sherborn (now Avon) and Yeovil (Somerset).

Ammonites tuberculatus. 'Lower Chalk', Norton. 'Greensand', Rundaway Hill and Chute Farm, near Warminster, Wiltshire,

Ammonites undulatus. 'Marlstone' (Middle Lias). Somerset Coal Canal.

Turritella trilineata. 'Norwich Crag', Bramerton, Norfolk.

Astarte ovata. 'Oak-Tree Clay', North Wiltshire Canal and several other localities in Somerset and Northamptonshire.

Avicula costata. 'Clay over the Upper Oolite (Bradford Clay)', several localities including Stony Stratford, Buckinghamshire.

Avicula echinata. 'Cornbrash', south-west of Tellisford, Somerset.

Chama crassa. 'Clay over the Upper Oolite' (Bradford Clay), Stoford. Somerset [or Wiltshire?].

Chama striata. 'Oak-Tree Clay', Bagley Wood Pit and North Wiltshire Canal.

Clavicula cucumerina. 'Chalk', Surrey. 'Coral Rag', Longleat Park near Warminster, Wiltshire and Derry Hill. The same species as Mantell's later-named *sceptrifera*.

Galea. With the exception of *Clavicula*, listed above, this is the only generic name published validly for the first time in Smith's list.

Modiola anatina. 'Fuller's Earth Rock', Ancliff.

Mya intersectans. 'Fuller's Earth Rock'. No locality mentioned.

Mytilus tunicatus. 'Clay over the Upper Oolite (Bradford Clay)', Combhay, [now] Avon,

Ostrea nigosa. 'Fuller's Earth Rock', Monkton Combe, [now] Avon, Tucking Mill and elsewhere.

Pecten sexcostatus. 'Greensand'. Chute Farm.

Terebratula reticulata. 'Clay over the Upper Oolite'. Several localities including Winsley, Wiltshire.

Trigonia curvirostra. 'Oak-Tree (Kimmeridge) Clay, North Wiltshire Canal and 'Coral Rag', Longleat Park.

Appendix 2

Principal Publications and Manuscripts by William Smith

(A number of the following are reproduced *in extenso* in *William Smith: his Maps and Memoirs*, Sheppard, T., London, 1917 (reprinted 1920)).

1794 *Plan of the Proposed Somersetshire Coal Canal*, Cary, London. Described in *John Cary, Engraver, Map, Chart and Print Seller and Globe Maker. 1754 to 1835*. Fordham H.G., Cambridge, 1935, 96-99, 103-6, 107-8.

1794 Plan of the Proposed Deviations of the Somersetshire Coal Canal, Cary, London. As above, 53.

1796 MS. List of 23 English strata from the Chalk to the Coal.

1796 MS. *Strata in general and their position.*

1797 MS. *Locality of Plants, Insects, Birds &c. arises from the nature of the strata.*

1797 MS. *Natural order of the Strata or Structure of the Earth deduced from practical Observations from which are also drawn some Remarks on the Deluge part 2nd.* Published by Douglas, J.A. and Cox, L.R. in the Geology Magazine, 1949, 86.

1799 *A Map of Five miles round the City of Bath*. Taylor and Nayler, Bath. 1_ inches to 1 mile. Coloured geologically. Almost certainly the oldest geological map in existence. Presented to the Geological Society of London, 1831.

1799 *Table of Strata* (near Bath). Dictated by Smith at 29 Great Pulteney Street, Bath. Proc. Yorks. Geol. Soc., 19, Pl.10.

1800 A geological map connecting the structure of the north of England with that of the south-western districts, delineating the whole oolitic series across the country. In the possession of John Phillips in 1831, but apparently now lost.

1801 *General Map of the Strata found in England and Wales*. Presented to the Geological Society of London, 1831.

1801 MS. Plan of Smith's first Prospectus. In the possession of the Geological Society of London. More legible copies in the Society's Library, and the libraries of the Science Museum, the Natural History Museum and the British Museum.

1801 *Prospectus of a Work entitled Accurate Delineations and Descriptions of the Natural Order of the various Strata that are found in different parts of England and Wales: with Practical Observations thereon.* Printed by McMillan, London. Presented to the Geological Society of London, 1831.

1805 *Map of Somersetshire*. Apparently now lost.

1805 Account of the improvement of Prisley Bog, in six parts. *Trans. Soc. Arts*, 23, 148-172.

1806 *The Improvement of Boggy Land by Irrigation, as carried into Effect. Journ. Nat. Phil.*, 15, 302-313.

1806 *A Treatise on Irrigation. (Observations on the Utility, Form and Management of Water Meadows, and the Draining and Irrigating of Peat Bogs, with An Account of Prisley Bog, and other Extraordinary Improvements, conducted for His Grace the Duke of Bedford, Thomas William Coke, Esq., M.P. and others)*. Harding, London.

1806 *Notice of Mr. Smith's Work on the Strata of England and Wales. Agricultural Mag., ser. 2*, 1, 21-22.

1807 *Description of Norfolk, its Soil and Substrata*. Norwich. Partly printed - not completed or published.

1811 *Reports of Mr. William Smith and Mr. Martin, on the Strata of the Collieries at and near Nailsea*. Bristol.

1815 *A Delineation of the Strata of England and Wales, with part of Scotland; exhibiting The Collieries and Mines, the Marshes and Fen Lands originally overflowed by the Sea, and the Varieties of Soil according to the Variations in the Substrata, Illustrated by the most descriptive names by W. Smith*. Cary, London. About 400 copies made, less than 100 extant. One hangs in Burlington House (the Geological Society of London).

1815 *A Memoir to the Map and Delineation of the Strata of England and Wales, with part of Scotland.* Cary, London. (Includes a description of the geology of Yorkshire).

1815 (Observations on his Map). *Trans. Soc. Arts*, 23, 53-58.

1816 *Strata identified by Organized Fossils, containing Prints on Coloured Paper of the most Characteristic specimens in each Stratum.* Sowerby (and others), London.

1817 *Section of Strata, North Wilts*. (London) Lithographed section sold by Smith.

1817 *Strata South of London, dipping northwards*. (London). Lithographed section sold by Smith.

1817 *Stratigraphical System of Organized Fossils with reference to the specimens of The Original Geological Collection in the British Museum: explaining their state of preservation and their use in identifying the British Strata*. Williams, London.

1817-19 *Geological Table of British Organised Fossils* and a series of geological sections. Cary, London. (Includes a *'Geological Section from London to Snowdon, showing the of Varieties of the Strata, and the correct altitudes of the Hills')*.

1817 *Table of the Distribution of Ammonites, drawn up by John Phillips, under the direction of William Smith. Quart. Journ. Geol. Soc., 1860*, 16.

1818 *Statement of Facts* (addressed to the Committees of Management for the Diss Navigation). London.

1818 MS. *Geology of England. Mr. Wm. Smith's Claims*. In Smith's small legible handwriting. 14 pages, lithographed.

1819 *Proposed Aire and Dunn Canal to drain the contiguous lands and to shorten and connect the present navigation.* (Plan). Lithograph reproduced in *The Naturalist*, 1912, 282.

1819 -26 *New Geological Atlas of England and Wales*. Cary, London. Published in six parts covering twenty counties, including Yorkshire in four sections.

1820 *A New Geological Map of England and Wales, with the Inland Navigations; exhibiting The Districts of Coal and other sites of Mineral Tonnage*. Cary, London.

1824 *A New Geological Map of England and Wales.* Cary, London.

1827 *Gifts to the York Museum. Yorks. Phil.Soc. Report for 1826.*

1827 MS. Letter to Sir John Johnstone regarding the development of Scarborough.

1827 *On retaining Water in the Rocks for Summer Use.* An article on Scarborough's water supply in the *Philosophical Magazine*, New Series, 1, No. 6, 415.

1829 *Stratification in Hackness Hills*. Day, London. A map - some copies coloured by Smith.

1830 M.S. *Memoir of the Stratification of the Hackness Hills,* annexed to the map.

1830 *On Coal.* Reviewed in *The Whitby Repository*, 6, 370-372.

1830 MS. *Elective Attractions by Solution*. (Observations in Chemistry). Acquired by the Scarborough Society.

1831 MS. *Agriculture. An investigation of circumstances relating to the present ill-success of farming.* (Mostly in shorthand). Acquired by the Scarborough Society.

1831? MS. *Politics, Statistics, &c.* Acquired by the Scarborough Society.

1832 *A Synopsis of Geological Phenomena*. A single folio sheet, printed in Oxford.

1835 *Deductions from Established Facts in Geology*. Scarborough.

1835? *Deductions from Established Facts in Geology relating to the Crust of the Globe, its former Associated Beings, Concomitant Events, & Superficial Changes*. Todd, Scarborough and Hailes, London.

1835 MSS. *Freestone* and *Building Stone*. (Notes on their properties, following Smith's work on the Royal Commission to select building stone for the Houses of Parliament). Published posthumously.

1837 *Practical Distinctions in Minerals. (Notice of a Method of easily distinguishing between minute grains of Quartz and Mica in 'Contents')*. Published in *The Magazine of Natural History* new series (usually known as *Charlesworth's Magazine*).

1837 *Coal Finding*. As above.

1838 *On the Variations in the Quantity of Rain which falls in different parts of the Earth. Rept. 8th Meeting Brit. Assoc. Adv. Sci., Trans. Sections,* 27-28. Also *The Atheneum,* 1838, 650.

1839 *Abstract Views of Geology*. Partly printed, not completed or published.

Appendix 3

The William Smith Trail

For those who may be interested in finding extant relics of William Smith's life and work, the following may be useful:

Churchill, Oxfordshire: William Smith's birthplace, about twenty-five miles north-west of Oxford. It is situated on a hill, about 550 feet above sea level, and is graced by a fifteen-foot high monument to him (map reference: SF 282243). See p.146. The village today has a strong community spirit and more than fifty people wove tapestries between 1990 and 1993 to cover a large number of kneelers for the modern church, commemorating significant people and organisations in its history. Naturally, these included William Smith. A quarter of a mile to the north west of the monument is a chapel, a remnant of a medieval church, made redundant in 1985. As a millennium project, it is planned to open a museum in it.

Manor House, Stow-on-the-Wold: at the north end of Market Square (map reference: SP 192258).

Rugbourne Farm: thought by the present owner, Mr. Richard Knight, to date from the fifteenth century. A listed building of three storeys, with the top floor windows filled in, it remains almost unchanged since Smith lodged there (map reference: ST 651583).

Sapperton Tunnel: The Daneway Portal, in Gothic style, at the north-western end of the Sapperton Tunnel (map reference: SP 943033) was rebuilt in 1996 and is accessible by public footpath. At the other end, the Coates Portal, to a Classical design, was restored in 1977, and is just a few yards from a public house car park at the end of an unmade road (map reference: SP 966006). The tunnel is presently blocked by two large falls of rock and fuller's earth.

Combe Hay locks: seven of these derelict locks are accessible to the public today – a short walk under the old railway bridge from map reference ST 745604. They are generally in a poor state, but the Somersetshire Coal Canal Society, founded in 1992, aims to protect these and other remaining structures from further deterioration. They have no present ambition to restore the canal.

Bull's Nose, Combe Hay: identifiable at map reference ST 741612. A short climb up the hill brings you to the probable site of the engine house.

Midford Aqueduct: (map reference ST 748603), accessible by public footpath from Midford, near the old railway viaduct.

Tucking Mill House: Smith's home at map reference ST 766616.

Tucking Mill Cottage: the building on which the commemorative plaque was wrongly placed (map reference: ST 765615). On the site of the fuller's earth works behind the cottage, there is now a small reservoir belonging to Wessex Water, providing special facilities for disabled anglers. Do not park next to the small box near the gate, as this is for the disabled anglers to use a key to unlock it. The Somersetshire Coal Canal ran immediately in front of it on the other side of the road. Traces of the canal here are obliterated by rubbish infill.

Cottage Crescent, Bath: now Bloomfield Crescent, where Bloomfield Drive joins Bloomfield Road (map reference: ST 738629).

Trim Street, Bath: between Barton Street and John Street (map reference: ST 748650). No. 2 now houses an art dealer and No. 3 a sandwich bar.

Tramway from the Quarry at Kingham Field to Tucking Mill House: From map reference 766618 to 766616. At the north end there is a steep stairway (Bluebell Steps), so it is likely that an inclined plane would have been necessary to carry the stone down to the tramway. A public footpath follows its track, emerging by the side of Smith's house, where there was a wharf on the canal. Traces of stone sleepers and the situation of short sidings to serve minor stone workings can identified.

Scarborough Museum (Rotunda), Valley Road: map reference: TA 043883. The reversed reproduction of Phillips's section of the coast is painted on the frieze under the cupola, easily viewed from the mezzanine floor.

St. Peter's Church, Marefair, Northampton: erected around 1170 by Simon de St. Liz, first Norman Earl of Northampton. William Smith's unmarked grave is close to the west wall. Adjacent to Smith's bust inside the church is a tablet in the form of a scroll, commemorating George Baker, in whose house Smith died. Baker's remains, and those of his sister Ann, are interred in the family vault in King Street Chapel. The church is routinely locked for security reasons, but the key is available from the adjacent public house, The Old Black Lion.

Appendix 4

The Geological Periods

Cambrian: 590 to 505 Ma (million years ago)
Sediments deposited during the period include the first organisms with skeletons. Common fossils include brachiopods, trilobites, ostracods and, late in the period graptolites.

Ordovician: 505 to 438 Ma.
Named after an ancient Celtic tribe, the Ordovices. Noted for the presenceof various rapidly evolving graptolite genera and of the earliest jawless fish.

Silurian: 438 to 408 Ma.
The end of the period is marked by the climax of the Caledonian orogeny and the filling of several Palaeozoic basins of deposition.

Devonian: 408 to 360 Ma.
The period of the Old Red Sandstone. Abundant invertebrate fauna.

Carboniferous : 360 to 286 Ma.
Marine limestones with a rich coral brachiopod fauna. Vast forests gave rise to extensive coal measures.

Permian: 286 to 248 Ma
Corals, trilobites and blastoid echinoderms vanished at the end of this period in a mass extinction.

Triassic: 248 to 213 Ma.
Many new faunal and floral elements,including ammonites, modern corals, various molluscs, the dinosaurs and certain gymnosperms.

Jurassic: 213 to 144 Ma.
Clays, calcareous sandstones and limestones. Brachiopods, bivalves, ammonites and many other invertebrate stocks. Reptiles flourished on land and in the sea, but mammals were relatively insignificant and presumed to have been predominantly nocturnal. The first birds, including Archaeopteryx, appeared late in the period.

Cretaceous: 144 to 65 Ma:
Noted for the deposition of chalk and the mass extinction of many invertebrate and vertebrate stocks, including the dinosaurs, mososaurs, ichthyosaurs and plesiosaurs.

Tertiary: 65 to 2 Ma.

Quaternary: the last 2 million years:
Numerous major ice-sheet advances in the northern hemisphere.

Index